Stretch your KS2 SPaG skills with CGP!

This book is perfect for pupils aged 9-10 who are confident with the Grammar, Punctuation and Spelling skills they need for Year 5.

It's filled with challenging questions to help them gain a deeper understanding of each topic. We've also included mixed practice quizzes and a test at the end so pupils' strengths and weaknesses can be assessed.

And there's more! Everything is perfectly matched to the National Curriculum and you'll find answers to every question at the back. Enjoy!

What CGP is all about

Our sole aim here at CGP is to produce the highest quality books — carefully written, immaculately presented and dangerously close to being funny.

Then we work our socks off to get them out to you — at the cheapest possible prices.

Contents

Grammar

Section 1 – Word Classes

Nouns — Singular and Plural.....................4
Verb Agreement 6
Prepositions, Determiners and Pronouns 7
Noun or Verb?.................................8
Determiner or Pronoun?.....................10
Adjective or Adverb? 11

Section 2 – Verb Forms

The Past Perfect 12
Tenses in Written Speech 14
Modal Verbs 16
Verbs to show Character Motivation 18

Section 3 – Phrases and Clauses

Relative Clauses..............................21
More about Relative Clauses.....................22
Fronted Adverbials..............................24
Fronted Adverbials for Effect....................26

Section 4 – Linking Ideas

Linking Ideas with Conditional Clauses 28
Linking Ideas: Conjunctions and Adverbs.....30
Linking Ideas in Fiction Writing 31
Linking Ideas in Arguments 33

Section 5 – Writing Style

Repetition in Fiction Writing......................36
Useful Techniques in Non-Fiction Writing.....38
Non-Standard English in Written Speech 40

End of Grammar Quiz

End of Grammar Quiz...........................42

Punctuation

Section 6 – Sentence Punctuation

End of Sentence Punctuation 44
Parenthesis 46
Abbreviations..48

Section 7 – Commas and Apostrophes

Commas Around Embedded Clauses...........49
Commas with Co-ordinating Conjunctions ...50
Commas to Avoid Confusion 52
Commas Between Adjectives.....................54
Punctuating Interjections 55
Commas for Places and Dates...................56
Apostrophes.. 57
Homophones involving Apostrophes............58
Apostrophes — Tricky Plurals...................59

Section 8 – Punctuation for Speech

Punctuating Speech.................................60
Reported Speech to Direct Speech.............63
Direct Speech to Reported Speech.............64

Section 9 – Paragraphs and Layout

Paragraph Structure 66
Paragraphs: New Speaker, New Line 68

End of Punctuation Quiz

End of Punctuation Quiz..........................70

Contents

Spelling

Section 10 – Prefixes

Number Prefixes from Latin...................... 72
Prefixes: 'mini' and 'micro'...................... 73
Prefixes: 'bene' and 'mal' 74
Prefixes: 'ultra' and 'hyper' 75
Prefix: 'fore'.. 76

Section 11 – Word Endings and Suffixes

Suffixes: Changing to Verbs 77
Suffixes: the Sounds of 'shus' and 'shul'..... 78
Suffixes: 'ant', 'ent' and their variants 80

Section 12 – Confusing Words

Words Containing 'ei' and 'ie' 83
Words Containing Double Consonants......... 84
Silent Letters... 86
The Many Sounds of 'ough' 87

End of Spelling Quiz

End of Spelling Quiz 88

End of Book Test

End of Book Test.......................................90

Glossary...96
Answers 98

Published by CGP
Written by Joanna Copley and John Svatins
Editors: Keith Blackhall, Eleanor Claringbold, Christopher Lindle, Sam Norman, Gabrielle Richardson,
Hannah Roscoe and Caroline Thomson
With thanks to Jan Greenway for the copyright research.

A note for teachers, parents and caregivers
Just something to bear in mind if you're choosing further reading for Year 5 pupils — all the extracts in this book are suitable
for children of this age, but we can't vouch for the full texts they're taken from, or other works by the same authors.

ISBN: 978 1 78294 947 3

Clipart from Corel®
Printed by Elanders Ltd, Newcastle upon Tyne.
Based on the classic CGP style created by Richard Parsons.

Nouns – Singular and Plural

Most nouns can be singular (one) or plural (more than one).

one cat/two cats   one fox/two foxes

To form a plural from a singular, you usually add -s or -es.
Some nouns don't follow this pattern though — they have irregular plurals.

tooth/teeth   goose/geese   mouse/mice   man/men   leaf/leaves

1 Write a sentence which includes a <u>singular</u> and a <u>plural</u> noun.
<u>Underline</u> the singular noun, and <u>circle</u> the plural noun.

....

....

2 All the nouns below have <u>irregular plurals.</u> Fill in the tables by writing
in the missing <u>singular</u> or <u>plural</u> nouns. Use a dictionary to help you.

Singular	Plural
woman	....
series	....
calf	....
loaf	....
....	people
....	crises
....	cacti
....	spacecraft

Singular	Plural
axis	....
sheep	....
criterion	....
....	lice
....	fish
....	bacteria
....	deer
....	indices

Nouns which can be singular or plural are called countable nouns.
Some nouns don't work in the plural. These are called non-countable nouns.
For example, you can't talk about 'traffics'.

traffic   tennis   rice

Abstract nouns tend
to be non-countable.

health   happiness   knowledge

3 Circle the nouns that are <u>non-countable</u>.

Hint — try putting it into the plural. If it sounds weird, it's probably a non-countable noun.

furniture   chair   information

spoon   bread   apple   spade   help   desk   train

office   funeral   honesty   heart   fun   game   eye

penny   advice   letter   magazine   suitcase   bed   gold

4 Read the sentences below. Explain why the underlined noun can be either <u>countable</u> or <u>non-countable</u>, depending on the sense in which it is used.

<u>Cheese</u> is a good source of calcium.
France produces many different <u>cheeses</u>.

....

....

....

5 Write two sentences using the word 'sugar' — one using it as a <u>countable</u> noun, and one using it as a <u>non-countable</u> noun.

....

....

How did you find these different
types of nouns? Tick a box.

Verb Agreement

Verbs change depending on who is doing the action.
This is called verb agreement.

A cow jumps over the moon.

'Cow' is a singular noun,
so the verb takes an 's'.

Two cows jump over the moon.

'Cows' is a plural noun,
so the verb has no 's'.

1 Circle the underline{correct verb} for each of the following sentences.

Emily eat / eats cereal every day for breakfast.

The children call / calls loudly to their friends to come and play.

Seven deer run / runs out into the meadow to eat the grass.

2 Add your own verbs to the sentences below, making sure they **agree** with the noun or nouns doing the action.

Meg and Suki .... a film together every Sunday.

The Sahara Desert .... from the Red Sea to the Atlantic Ocean.

3 Write three sentences about things that happen every day at your school. In each sentence, underline{circle} the verb and underline{underline} the noun or nouns it agrees with.

1. ....

2. ....

3. ....

How did you find verb agreement? Tick a box.

Prepositions, Determiners and Pronouns

It's easy to get confused between prepositions, determiners and pronouns. Here's a summary:

A **preposition** tells you the position of a noun. ➔ | on the bed | by the sink |

A **determiner** tells you how specific or general a noun is. ➔ | his pen | a house |

A **pronoun** takes the place of a noun. ➔ | He likes tennis. | Richard hates it. |

1 Underline all the words which belong to the **word class** in brackets.

I went to the seaside for a week.   (Preposition)

Do you know whose books the caretaker found?   (Determiner)

This is my favourite. I like yours too though.   (Pronoun)

2 Swap the words belonging to the word classes shown in **brackets** to **different** words of the **same class**. The first sentence is an example.

They wanted to sail on the lake.

(verb and preposition) *They loved to swim in the lake.*

I gave my money to Eva.

(pronoun and determiner) ....

(verb and preposition) ....

(determiner and common noun) ....

Were you able to identify and use prepositions, determiners and pronouns correctly? Tick a box.

Section 1 — Word Classes

Noun or Verb?

Lots of words can act as a noun or a verb in a sentence.
If you try swapping it with other words, it will tell you which type of word it is.

> The train was late.

The nouns 'bus', 'taxi' and 'plane' could all be used
in place of 'train'. So here, 'train' must be a noun.

> If we train every day, we'll win.

The verbs 'run', 'jump' and 'swim' could all be used
in place of 'train'. So here, 'train' must be a verb.

1 Circle '<u>noun</u>' or '<u>verb</u>' to categorise the underlined word in each sentence.

> Think about what the underlined word in each sentence could be swapped for. It doesn't need to make sense — it just needs to work grammatically.

The bad <u>cut</u> on my knee needed three stitches. ⟶ noun / verb

Last Saturday, we went to the big football <u>match</u>. ⟶ noun / verb

My brother played the <u>part</u> of Hook in 'Peter Pan'. ⟶ noun / verb

I <u>hug</u> my Grandma every day when I see her. ⟶ noun / verb

They decided to <u>paint</u> the door a different colour. ⟶ noun / verb

The plane began to <u>bank</u> left. ⟶ noun / verb

I like your crimson <u>dress</u>; it really suits you. ⟶ noun / verb

Oh dear, that's a nasty <u>fall</u> you've had there! ⟶ noun / verb

If you need to leave, just <u>excuse</u> yourself and go. ⟶ noun / verb

I'd <u>guard</u> that door if I were you: it's unlocked. ⟶ noun / verb

2 Choose <u>four</u> words from the box, and use each one as a <u>noun</u> in one sentence and a <u>verb</u> in another.

~~permit~~   light   order   plant   stamp   photograph   water

Example:
(verb) I will not <u>permit</u> you to go to the party at Joe's tomorrow.
(noun) He needs a parking <u>permit</u> to stay there for more than an hour.

1. (verb) ....

   (noun) ....

2. (verb) ....

   (noun) ....

3. (verb) ....

   (noun) ....

4. (verb) ....

   (noun) ....

3 Think of your own example of a word which could be used as a <u>noun</u> <u>or a verb</u>. Use it as a noun in one sentence and a verb in another.

My word is: ....

(verb) ....

....

....

(noun) ....

....

....

Were you able to identify whether words are being used as nouns or verbs and use them correctly? Tick a box.

Determiner or Pronoun?

Some words can act as a determiner or a pronoun.
You have to look at the job the word is doing in the sentence.

He loves these sausages.

Here, 'these' tells you something about the noun. It must be a determiner.

These are my favourites.

Here, 'these' is used in place of a noun. It must be a pronoun.

Remember, determiners come **before** nouns. Pronouns **replace** nouns.

1 Circle '<u>determiner</u>' or '<u>pronoun</u>' to describe the underlined word in each sentence.

<u>Those</u> pens are really nice to write with. ➡ determiner / pronoun

<u>This</u> is something I'm not willing to do. ➡ determiner / pronoun

Luckily my bag is not as heavy as <u>his</u>. ➡ determiner / pronoun

<u>Which</u> road will take us back to Nottingham? ➡ determiner / pronoun

2 Use each word given below in <u>two sentences</u> — one using it as a <u>determiner</u>, and one using it as a <u>pronoun</u>.

many ....
....

some ....
....

any ....
....

Were you able to work out whether words are being used as determiners or pronouns? Tick a box.

Adjective or Adverb?

Some words can act as an adjective or an adverb.
It depends on what the word is doing in the sentence.

I bought a fast car.

Here, 'fast' is describing
a noun (a car).
It must be an adjective.

I drove my car very fast.

Here, 'fast' is describing
a verb (how I drove).
It must be an adverb.

1 Circle 'adjective' or 'adverb' to categorise the underlined word in the sentence.

I make sure I see my grandad <u>weekly</u>. ⟶ adjective / adverb

I fetch my grandad's <u>weekly</u> newspaper for him. ⟶ adjective / adverb

We had to stand completely <u>still</u>. ⟶ adjective / adverb

After an hour, I was <u>still</u> waiting for him. ⟶ adjective / adverb

The axis of that graph you drew is not <u>straight</u>. ⟶ adjective / adverb

You must go <u>straight</u> home without looking back. ⟶ adjective / adverb

2 Use each word given below in <u>two sentences</u> — one using it as an <u>adjective</u>, and one using it as an <u>adverb</u>.

For this first one, remember that adverbs can describe adjectives too.

pretty ....

....

hard ....

....

Were you able to identify whether words are being used as adjectives or adverbs? Tick a box.

Section 2 — Verb Forms

The Past Perfect

You already know lots of forms of present and past tenses.
There is one more to learn — the past perfect.

	Present	Past
Simple	I jump	I jumped
Progressive	I am jumping	I was jumping
Perfect	I have jumped	I had jumped

This is the past perfect. It always uses 'had',
followed by a past tense form of the main verb.

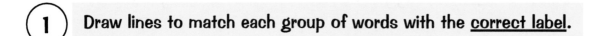

1 Draw lines to match each group of words with the <u>correct label</u>.

She had achieved	simple past	We are recommending
You are deciding	past progressive	I was accompanying
He was suggesting	past perfect	I have guaranteed
I have persuaded	present progressive	She had recognised
We interrupted	present perfect	You exaggerated

Different verb forms let you show a sequence of events through time.

12 noon   3 pm   6 pm

Even earlier   Earlier   Now

It has rained today. (present perfect)

At 3 pm, it rained. (simple past)

At 12 noon, it had not rained. (past perfect)

2 Complete your own pictures and sentences to show a <u>sequence</u>.
Include an example of the present perfect, the simple past and the past perfect.

12 noon   3 pm   6 pm

.... today. (present perfect)

At 3 pm .... (......................................)

At 12 noon .... (......................................)

3 Write a short passage about <u>learning to do something</u>. What did you feel
like <u>before</u> you could do it, <u>while</u> you were learning and <u>after</u> you'd finished?
Write the number of different <u>verb forms</u> you have used in the box.

....

....

....

....

....

How well can you identify and use different past tense
forms, including the past perfect? Tick a box.

Tenses in Written Speech

Stories are usually written in the simple past tense.

> Jenny took a deep breath and yelled, "Come here, quickly!"

But when speech is put into a story, it's often in the simple present tense because it is happening within the story.

> "What's the matter?" her mum called back. "Is there a problem?"
> "There isn't right now," shouted Jenny, "but there will be in a minute!"

The simple past tense verb forms are in green, and the simple present tense verb forms are in red.

'Will' is a simple present tense modal verb used to describe what is going to happen in the future.

1   Underline the <u>past tense verb forms</u>, and circle the <u>other verb forms</u>.

"I will be going to the park soon," called Tom. "Will you come too?"

"I didn't take the dog out this morning, but I will do it later," said John.

Helen shouted, "Tidy up your mess! I'm sick of it."

"I haven't had breakfast," moaned Dad. "Do we have to go out now?"

"I bought the game you wanted, so we will play it later," said Dariush.

"Last night, when I went outside, the slugs were eating all my lettuces," said Mum, crossly. "So tonight I will sit out there with a torch, and when they attack the plants I will be ready for them with my bucket."

2   Write a sentence that includes <u>speech</u>, using as many verb forms as you can.

....

....

A reporting clause is the clause which tells you who is speaking. It should be in the same tense as the story narrative.

This narrative is in the past tense, so the reporting clause 'said Sam' is also in the past tense.

The spoken sentences are in a mixture of present and past tense verb forms.

> The trees were creaking eerily, the wind was screaming through their branches and on the horizon, storm clouds blotted out the sunset. "This weather is ridiculous," said Sam, as he struggled to open his umbrella. "We only came out to do a bit of shopping. If I had known we were going to be on the set of a horror film, I would have stayed at home."

3 Write down the names of four verb forms that are used in the passage above. Give an example from the passage of each form.

....

....

....

....

4 What is always true about the tense of the narrative and the reporting clause?

....

5 What verb forms can you use when a character speaks?

....

How did you find using tenses in written speech? Tick a box.

Modal Verbs

Modal verbs show certainty, ability and obligation (having to do something).
The pink verbs in the sentences below are all modal verbs.

**Certainty
(or uncertainty):** If he carries on, he might break the window.

Ability: I can carry that, if it's too heavy for you.

Obligation: You really should take down your Christmas decorations.

Here are the main modal verbs:

can   may   shall   will   must

could   might   should   would

---

1 Circle the phrases below which include modal verbs.

I would be   She has been   They might think

You may go   He runs   You wrote   We could take

I see   Would you like   She should never   We may not

They think   I shouldn't   We could, perhaps   I said

---

2 You're invited to a party. You want to go, but you're not sure if you can.
Write a sentence using as many modal verbs as you can to explain this.

....

....

....

3 Complete these sentences with a clause using a **modal verb**.

If you swim in that lake, you ....

Ask your mum for some chocolate. She ....

If you tried, I am sure ....

I .... if I were you!

He .... if he had any.

4 Rewrite the sentences below, using a variety of **modal verbs**. The first one has been done for you.

You think you want to watch a film, but you are worried it's too scary.

I could watch that film, but it might be too scary. ....

You are considering going shopping, but maybe the shops are closed.

....

You are not sure whether or not your dad said you were allowed sweets.

....

You want to go on holiday, but does your mum have enough money?

....

You don't think it's a good idea to take your bike in case it's stolen.

....

Gran said she did not want you to watch TV, but you are determined to.

....

How well do you understand what modal verbs are and how to use them in sentences? Tick a box.

Verbs to show Character Motivation

Verbs can tell your reader what your character is thinking and feeling. This is called their motivation. As well as using modal verbs, you can use different tenses to show how your character's motivation changes over time.

1 **Read this passage and answer the questions about it below.**

> "If I had realised it was so easy to tie my own tie," said Sara, "I would have learned how to do it ages ago. I think I might teach my brother how to do it, because he is always keen to learn new things."

Give two modal verbs used in the passage. ....

Give two examples of other verbs used, and name the verb forms.

....

....

Name the verb form used in the reporting clause. ....

2 **Write a short sentence using each of the verb forms and verbs below.**

past progressive of 'feel': ....

....

present perfect of 'think': ....

....

past perfect of 'want': ....

....

a modal verb with 'stop': ....

....

3 Complete each sentence using an <u>appropriate form</u> of the <u>verb in brackets</u>. You may need a modal verb.

If she (see) .... them, I am sure she would have stopped.

Since he (tell) .... me that, I can't think of anything else.

If I'd known, I (help) .... her.

Before you go, you (tidy up) .... the mess in here.

If he did it, then he (own up) .... to what he did.

4 Change the verb form of the <u>underlined verbs</u> so the passage makes sense.

I am not staying here any longer, thought Tam. I <u>am</u> .... a servant for long enough. It <u>has been</u> .... time I <u>will make</u> .... my own way in the world.

So that night, he <u>steals</u> .... out of the house and <u>will creep</u> .... to the boatshed. Even though it <u>be</u> .... hard to sail the boat, he <u>was knowing</u> .... it was his only chance. This time he <u>will</u> .... succeed.

5 Underline all the <u>past tense</u> verb forms, and circle the <u>modal verbs</u>.

If he hadn't been so desperate, he would never have managed it.

And if he had not had his knife with him, he might have given up.

The ropes holding the boat were stiff, and he was sawing at them for ages

before they parted. If I didn't have the knife, I could still have been stuck

here at dawn, he thought grimly to himself. At last, however, he hauled

the tattered sail up, got into the old boat and pushed out to sea.

6 Label each <u>verb form</u> used below. (If it is a modal verb, just put 'modal verb'.)

The boat <u>had sprung</u> a leak: Tam <u>could</u> see that it <u>was filling</u> with water.

I<u>'m</u> sure it<u>'s getting</u> higher and higher, he <u>said</u> to himself.

7 Write a continuation of Tam's story. Try to include some dialogue. Show Tam's thoughts and feelings by using <u>modal verbs</u> and a variety of <u>verb forms</u>.

....

....

....

....

....

....

....

....

Verbs I have used which show Tam's thoughts and feelings are ....

....

....

....

How did you find using modal verbs and tenses to show a character's motivation? Tick a box.

 ☑   ☑   ☑

Relative Clauses

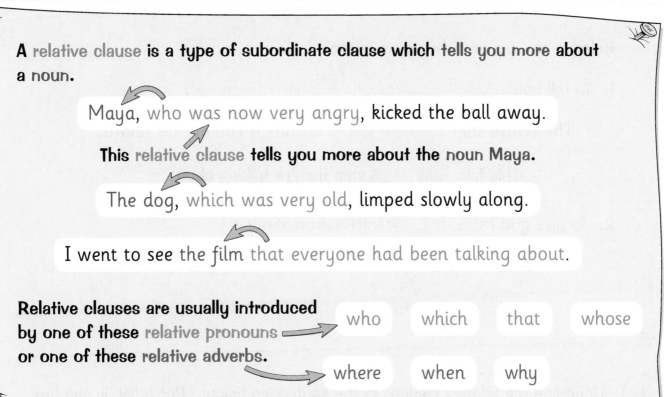

A relative clause is a type of subordinate clause which tells you more about a noun.

Maya, who was now very angry, kicked the ball away.

This relative clause tells you more about the noun Maya.

The dog, which was very old, limped slowly along.

I went to see the film that everyone had been talking about.

Relative clauses are usually introduced by one of these relative pronouns or one of these relative adverbs.

who   which   that   whose

where   when   why

1 Underline the relative clauses in the sentences below, and circle the nouns they are telling you more about.

The cat, which was clearly frightened, ran quickly out of the room.

The singer, who had a terrible cold, couldn't reach the top note.

Rocks that have got wet are slippery and dangerous.

I am now friends with Saba, whose sister I also know.

2 Add your own relative clauses to the sentences below.

Freddie, ..., lives next door to me.

The book, ..., was really good.

He had never been to Lincoln, ...

How did you find relative clauses? Tick a box.

More about Relative Clauses

Nice clause...

Relative clauses have two main uses:

1. **To tell you** which thing or person is being referred to:

> The cruise ship that we sailed on has a cinema on board.

This tells you which ship they're talking about.

2. **To give you** extra, non-essential information:

> Our cruise ship, which was built last year, has a swimming pool.

This is extra information.

1 Underline the <u>relative clauses</u> in the sentences below. Put a '**W**' in the box if the information in the relative clause is telling you <u>which</u> thing or person is being referred to, or put an '**E**' if it is giving you <u>extra</u> information.

The ball that belonged to Hamid was thrown over the fence. ☐

Joe, who was very tired, fell asleep in the car going home. ☐

Dogs that are not trained properly can be dangerous. ☐

Cliffs which are undermined by the sea often collapse. ☐

Their group, which had been lagging behind the others, got lost. ☐

Amit, whose dad works on a farm, really loves animals. ☐

2 If you've done Question 1 correctly, you should notice something about the <u>punctuation</u> of the sentences you've marked with an '**E**'. What do you notice?

....

....

The relative pronoun 'that' can sometimes be missed out.

the book that I am reading   the book I am reading

These both mean the same thing and are both relative clauses.

Relative clauses that give extra information need to be separated from the main clause with commas:

Tim, who is quite tall, plays basketball.

3 Complete these sentences by adding a <u>relative clause</u> in which the <u>relative pronoun 'that'</u> has been missed out.

The lady .... was very kind.

The car .... broke down yesterday.

4 Add a relative clause to these sentences which adds <u>extra information</u>.

Remember to use commas in these ones.

The holidays .... were a distant memory.

The lazy kitten .... quickly fell asleep.

5 Explain the <u>difference in meaning</u> between the two sentences below.

Children who can't read maps may get lost.
Children, who can't read maps, may get lost.

The first sentence implies ....

....

The second sentence implies ....

....

How well do you understand what relative clauses are used for, and can you identify and use them? Tick a box.

Fronted Adverbials

Adverbials **show you** how, when, where, why or how often **something happens. Fronted adverbials come at the start of the sentence.**

how **(manner)** ⟹ Somewhat theatrically, he sat and cried.

when **(time)** ⟹ Before the sun rose, he sat and cried.

where **(place)** ⟹ Under the station clock, he sat and cried.

why **(cause)** ⟹ Because of the pain, he sat and cried.

how often **(frequency)** ⟹ Nearly every day, he sat and cried.

1 **Match the <u>adverbials</u> to the <u>information</u> they're giving you.**

After dinner,  In desperation,

Forty miles away,  Only occasionally,

Nearly always, That very morning,

Due to the heat, For that reason,

His hands trembling, Whenever she could,

Out in the rain,  Like a panther,

2 Rewrite the sentences below, <u>moving the adverbial</u> to the <u>front</u> of the sentence. The first one has been done for you.

The forest lay devastated after the great storm was over.

.... After the great storm was over, the forest lay devastated. ....

Mel swam in the lake whenever she could.

....

The bull charged at us without any warning at all.

....

3 Look at the short sentences in the box. <u>Choose one</u>, and add <u>each</u> <u>category</u> of <u>fronted adverbial</u> to it. An example has been done for you.

> ... she left him behind.   ... they ran away.   ... he went on holiday.

(Manner) ... With sadness and regret, she left him behind. ....

(Manner) ....

(Time) ....

(Place) ....

(Cause) ....

(Frequency) ....

4 Write a sentence of your own using a <u>fronted adverbial</u>.

....

....

How did you find fronted adverbials? Tick a box.   ☹ ✓   ☺ ✓   😉 ✓

Section 3 — Phrases and Clauses

Fronted Adverbials for Effect

You can use fronted adverbials to paint vivid pictures with your writing.

With a mighty roar, the man dived on top of me.

The fronted adverbial is dramatic, and helps the reader imagine the scene.

You can also use fronted adverbials to set up a contrast.

Although some people think it's unimportant, I believe it is essential.

By acknowledging the disagreement first, the writer can finish the sentence with what he or she really believes.

1 Add a <u>fronted adverbial</u> to each of these sentences to <u>paint a vivid picture</u>. The first one has been done for you.

.....His hands shaking with excitement....., he opened the letter.

...., Anna was not in the least bit tired.

...., I drew on the wall to pass the time.

...., Jamal attacked the kidnappers.

...., the sailor exclaimed, 'There it is!'

...., the boat glided into the distance.

...., Sara slumped to her knees.

2 Choose one of your <u>adverbials</u> from Question 1, and explain the <u>effect</u> it has on the sentence.

....

....

3 These fronted adverbials set up a <u>contrast</u>. Complete each sentence. The first one has been done for you.

Despite working on it for hours, ...we still hadn't finished the task...........

Although healthy eating may seem boring, ...

Far from being a waste of time, ...

In spite of their objections, ...

However loud you shout, ...

4 Add a fronted adverbial to each sentence below. You decide whether you're <u>painting a picture</u> or setting up a <u>contrast</u>. The first one has been done for you.

...........Whether I liked it or not..........., I was forced to agree with him.

...., he ran for his life.

...., I disagree with you completely.

...., Sandy hid under the dusty bed.

...., other people prefer Maths.

5 Create <u>two</u> sentences of your own with <u>fronted adverbials</u> — one to <u>paint a picture</u> and one to set up a <u>contrast</u>.

....

....

....

....

How well can you use fronted adverbials to paint a picture or set up a contrast? Tick a box.

Section 4 — Linking Ideas

Linking Ideas with Conditional Clauses

Conditional clauses **are a type of** subordinate clause.
You use them to say what will happen if **something else happens.**
Here are some examples:

> If you don't go, you will regret it.
>
> Even if you go, you might still regret it.
>
> Provided that you go, I will go too.
>
> So long as you go, we can all go.
>
> Whether or not you go, I certainly won't.
>
> Unless you go, I don't want to.

Using conditional clauses shows that you can juggle ideas,
and imagine the consequences **of events which haven't yet happened.**

1 **Tick the box if the sentence contains a <u>conditional clause</u>.**

I will go to the fair with you tomorrow if you let me. ☐

Even if it is fine, I won't go with you to the fair tomorrow. ☐

We should go to the fair whether you want to or not. ☐

Provided that the weather is fine, we will go to the fair. ☐

I am not going to go to the fair tomorrow as I don't want to. ☐

I think we will go to the fair unless the weather is too cold. ☐

2 **Use two different types of <u>conditional clause</u> to complete the sentences below.**

...., I have no intention of helping her.

...., I shall definitely help her.

3 Rewrite the sentences below so they include a <u>conditional</u> clause. The first one has been done for you.

I am going to swim tomorrow as it will be sunny and warm.

<u>Provided that it is sunny and warm tomorrow, I'm going to swim.</u>

He will go to the football match when the car is mended.

....

You can wear my new scarf. You're not to get it dirty.

....

She is going to school. I know she may not want to, but she must.

....

4 Use <u>conditional clauses</u> to give your mum, dad or carer a list of <u>demands</u> for a new pair of shoes. Be as bossy as you like, and say what the <u>consequences</u> will be if the shoes aren't up to scratch.

Friendly hint — don't try this at home...

Some ideas for things to include in your list:
What type of shoe? Lace-ups, buckles, slip-ons?
What material? What colour? What size? What brand?

....

....

....

....

....

How did you find using conditional clauses to link ideas? Tick a box.

Linking Ideas: Conjunctions and Adverbs

Within a sentence, you can't join two clauses with an adverb.

> I played squash with my brother, afterwards I had a shower. ✗

This is incorrect. To write it correctly you either need to add a conjunction...

> I played squash with my brother, and afterwards I had a shower. ✓

... or write it as two sentences.

> I played squash with my brother. Afterwards I had a shower. ✓

1 Put a <u>tick</u> or a <u>cross</u> to show whether the clauses are <u>correctly linked</u>.

He tried several times, eventually he managed it. ☐

He tried several times, and eventually he managed it. ☐

He tried several times. Eventually, he managed it. ☐

They decided to have the party outside. Luckily, it stayed dry. ☐

They decided to have the party outside, luckily it stayed dry. ☐

They decided to have the party outside, and luckily it stayed dry. ☐

2 Link the two clauses below correctly using a <u>conjunction</u> plus an <u>adverb</u>.

It has been a cold spring, ... the garden hasn't grown much.

I expect he will be late .... there have been long delays on that road.

How did you find using conjunctions and adverbs to link ideas between and within sentences? Tick a box.

Linking Ideas in Fiction Writing

In stories, using adverbials to link ideas by time and place makes it clear to the reader what is happening when and where.

> Marek was stepping out of the post office, fiddling with his phone. All of a sudden, he noticed a man running out of the jeweller's on the other side of the road.

1 Read the text below. It contains lots of <u>adverbials showing time and place</u>. <u>Underline</u> them all, and then add each one to the correct box below.

The children had not been wild camping before, but they were looking forward to it. Sandy chose a flat, grassy spot, and then Jane put up the tent, while Peter sat nearby unpacking the mats and sleeping bags. After that, Sandy sorted out the food, so it was safe from the insects he could hear buzzing all around them.

They sat down in front of their new dwelling, and had a quick snack. After washing the plates in the stream a little way off, Jane and Peter went for a walk through the surrounding woods, gathering sticks for the fire which they would have that evening.

Meanwhile, back at the camp, Sandy had started to get the dinner ready.

<u>5 time adverbials</u>	<u>4 place adverbials</u>
before	all around them

<u>2 subordinate clauses showing time and place</u>

2 Order the events in the sentences by numbering them 1-4.
Then write a passage with the events <u>in order</u> and <u>add time links</u>
to show when things happened. <u>Underline</u> the links you've used.

They were watching some seals swimming nearby. ☐

They couldn't see a thing. ☐

It was starting to get foggy. ☐

Jane and Peter decided to go sailing in their new boat. ☐

....

....

....

....

3 Continue the story below by using adverbials of <u>time</u> and <u>place</u> to link ideas.

The fog was a white blanket. ....(place), Jane

could see walls of cloud. ....(time), they just sat,

shivering and miserable, and waited. It seemed to take hours, but

....(time) the wind rippled the soft clouds away,

and a watery sun shone. ....(place), they could

see a little island. ....(time), they reached it.

....(place), they saw exotic birds flying

....(place).

How did you find using adverbials of time and place
to link ideas in fiction writing? Tick a box. 🙂 ✓ 🙂 ✓ 🙂 ✓

Section 4 — Linking Ideas   © CGP — not to be photocopied

Linking Ideas in Arguments

When you're constructing an argument, you can link ideas by addition and contrast. This shows the reader the logic of what you're writing.

Homework can be excessively time-consuming for both students and parents. However, it can help students practise skills they learn in lessons. Moreover, it trains pupils to work more independently.

'However' introduces a contrasting idea.

'Moreover' adds another argument in favour of homework.

Other addition links:

and, also, as well as, furthermore, indeed, especially, in addition

Other contrast links:

but, alternatively, instead of, whereas, unlike, by contrast, although, on the other hand, while

---

(1) Insert a suitable <u>contrast</u> or <u>addition</u> link into each gap below.

Some think homework is a good idea, ... others don't.

I dislike maths lessons a lot, ... I like English lessons.

Mum likes me to do my homework straight away. ....,
she insists that I do it where she can see I'm actually working.

Homework helps you to revise what you've learned. ....,
it helps teachers check whether you've understood what they taught you.

.... some pupils don't enjoy
doing homework, it does help them to learn.

(2) Write a sentence of your own which includes a link of <u>contrast</u> or <u>addition</u>.

....

....

....

3 It's your turn to construct an argument about the question '<u>Do you think pupils should be allowed mobile phones in schools?</u>' To make your writing balanced, you will need to include arguments both <u>for</u> and <u>against</u>. Write them below.

<u>Arguments for</u> <u>having mobiles in school</u>	<u>Arguments against</u> <u>having mobiles in school</u>
They can be used for research.	They can cause envy between pupils.

4 Choose <u>two</u> arguments that are <u>for</u> having mobile phones, and link them with an <u>addition</u> link.

....

....

....

5 Choose at least <u>one</u> argument that is <u>for</u> having mobile phones, and at least <u>one</u> statement that is <u>against</u>. Link the two ideas with a <u>contrast</u> link.

....

....

....

A great way to link the paragraphs in an argument is by number.
This adds structure to your argument, making it sound more organised.

Firstly, ...   Secondly, ...   Thirdly, ...   Lastly, ...

These are useful adverbials to begin your final paragraph:

In conclusion, ...   All things considered, ...   In the end, ...

6 Write an argument, in <u>full paragraphs</u>, about the use of mobile phones in schools. You decide whether the main thrust of your argument will be <u>for</u> or <u>against</u>. Make sure you include plenty of links of <u>contrast</u>, <u>addition</u> and <u>number</u>.

....

....

....

....

....

....

....

....

....

....

How did you find linking ideas in arguments by contrast, addition and number? Tick a box.

Section 5 — Writing Style

Repetition in Fiction Writing

Repeating words, repeating verbs, and repeating certain types of phrases and clauses is a great way to create mood in your writing:

> It was a town where litter grew like deformed hedgerows, where police sirens sang like desperate nightingales, where street lamps mocked the ancient stars.

The repetition of relative clauses here sets the story's scene. The mood is eerie and unsettling. You can tell that this place might be dangerous.

1) Read the <u>two extracts</u> below. The first is part of a famous poem, and the second is taken from a famous novel. Explain the <u>mood</u> created by their repeated words, phrases and clauses.

"Cannon to right of them,
Cannon to left of them,
Cannon in front of them
Volleyed and thundered;"

An extract from 'The Charge
of the Light Brigade'
by Alfred, Lord Tennyson

....

....

....

....

....

....

"Fog everywhere. Fog up the river, fog down the river,
fog on the Essex marshes and fog on the Kentish heights,
fog creeping into ships, fog hovering on the rigging,
fog in the eyes and throats of ancient Chelsea pensioners."

An adapted extract from 'Bleak House' by Charles Dickens

....

....

....

2 Develop the phrases or clauses below with <u>repetition</u> to create the <u>mood</u> shown in brackets. The first one has been done for you.

(fantastical)   In a land where   *streams were strawberry squash, bushes*

were butterscotch bonbons and rocks were raspberry ripple ice cream.

(dangerous)   In caves where ....

....

(happy)   The king was as ....

....

(gloomy)   The weather was wild. Wind ....

....

3 Now use repetition of <u>words</u>, <u>phrases</u> and <u>clauses</u> to create a mood for the place in the question. Write the <u>mood</u> you have chosen in the box.

A seashore: (...........................)

....

....

....

An abandoned World War II bunker after dark: (...........................)

....

....

....

How did you find using repetition of words, phrases and clauses to create different moods? Tick a box.

Useful Techniques in Non-Fiction Writing

When you write non-fiction, you can use a variety of phrases and clauses to add information and make your sentences flow nicely.

> The River Severn flows for 220 miles, <u>which is just 5 miles longer than than Britain's second longest river, the Thames</u>. From its source at Plynlimon in Wales, the Severn flows through four counties, <u>finally reaching the sea at the muddy estuary north of Bristol</u>.

Relative clause — gives extra information about the length of the river.

Fronted adverbial — tells you where the river starts.

Subordinate clause — describes the end of the river's journey.

Expanded noun phrase — gives more information about the estuary.

(1) Read the text below. Label each coloured <u>phrase</u> or <u>clause</u> using a term from the black box and <u>briefly explain</u> what it does in the sentence.

> Subordinate clause   Expanded noun phrase
>   Relative clause   Fronted adverbial

....
....
....

....
....
....

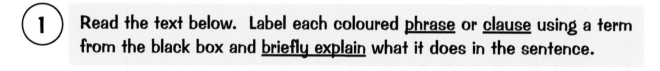

During the 19th century, the Lake District became popular with tourists, who visited the area <u>after reading</u> Wordsworth's poetry about <u>its wild, romantic beauty</u>.

....
....
....

....
....
....

2 In the box are some <u>notes</u> about the River Thames. Use these notes or anything else you know about the Thames to write a passage which contains a variety of <u>phrases</u> and <u>clauses</u>.

- It's the second longest river in the UK.
- Its source is at Thameshead in the Cotswold Hills.
- It reaches the sea at Southend-on-Sea.
- It flows through London, England's capital city.
- At the estuary, the river is tidal.
- There have been settlements along its banks for thousands of years.
- Many writers have written stories and poems about it.

....

....

....

....

....

....

3 Identify two types of <u>clause</u> or <u>phrase</u> you used in Question 2. Say <u>why</u> you used each type.

....

....

....

....

How did you find using phrases and clauses to add extra information to non-fiction writing? Tick a box.

Non-Standard English in Written Speech

In general, you should write in Standard English.

You can use non-Standard English in written speech to show how a character actually speaks. It lets the reader 'hear' their real voice.

'Where's 'e to then? 'Cos he ain't 'ere!' ⟸ In Standard English, this would be: 'Where is he? Because he isn't here!'

1 Give the Standard English form for these <u>non-Standard</u> words.

gonna ....   gimme ....   'cos ....

c'mon ....   lemme ....   lotta ....

a'right ....   cuppa ....   innit ....

2 Using the examples above, re-write the following sentences in <u>non-Standard English</u>.

Think about how it might sound if a character says it at speed.

'I am going to hit you if you don't let me have it! Give the money to me.'

....

....

3 People use <u>different words</u> for things in <u>different parts of the country</u>. Write down what you <u>think</u> these <u>non-Standard words</u> might mean in the places shown below.

It doesn't matter if you've no idea — just make a guess.

wee ....   bairn ....

boggin' ....   owt ....

tidy ....   mardy ....

daps ....   blower ....

4 Think of some other words that are <u>local</u> to where you live. Write them down alongside the words that would be used in <u>Standard English</u>.

Local words		Standard English words
....	→	....
....	→	....
....	→	....
....	→	....

5 Write out the sentences in the box below in <u>Standard English</u>.

> "I don't wanna do no more work today, I been at it for hours. Lemme go an' play with me mates. C'mon, gimme a break, Mum!"

....

....

....

....

6 Explain <u>when</u> you should write in <u>standard</u> and <u>non-Standard English</u>, and <u>why</u>.

....

....

....

....

How well do you understand when and why you should use Standard and non-Standard English? Tick a box.

Section 5 — Writing Style

End of Grammar Quiz

(1) **Correct the underlined plural nouns.**

A serieses of environmental crisis has cut the number of deers.

....   ☐
1 mark

(2) **Give the word class of each underlined word.**

....

Water   the   plants   weekly   or   they   will   wilt.

....   ☐
1 mark

(3) **Circle the verbs in the present perfect form and underline the verbs that are in the past perfect form.**

"If I had gone to Dad's last weekend, we were going to

watch the match, but he had to go away instead," said Kai.

"Now he has broken his foot, so we can't go next weekend

either. We've both been unlucky."   ☐
1 mark

(4) **Add modal verbs into this sentence so it makes sense.**

I .... do my homework tonight, but I don't want to.

I .... leave it till tomorrow, or I .... just
do it on Sunday.   ☐
1 mark

(5) **Underline the relative clauses and add any missing punctuation.**

The weeds that were growing in the garden which was

enormous by the way had spread over all the flower beds.   ☐
1 mark

(6) Turn this pair of sentences into a <u>single sentence</u> which includes a <u>conditional clause</u>.

You can borrow my guitar. You'll need to look after it though.

....   1 mark

(7) Underline the <u>relative clause</u> and circle the <u>conditional clause</u>.

"Once I've fought this monster which has ravaged your village,

you will be safe," said the Prince, "provided that I can defeat him."   1 mark

(8) Join the two sentences below into one by changing the first sentence into a <u>subordinate clause</u>.

We walked up the hill. We sat down and ate lunch.

....   1 mark

(9) Underline the <u>adverbials of time</u> and <u>place</u>. Underneath each one label them with either a '<u>T</u>' (<u>adverbials of 'time'</u>) or '<u>P</u>' (<u>adverbials of 'place'</u>).

Jan stopped his lorry suddenly in the middle of the road.

When he got out, he could hear a helicopter overhead.   1 mark

(10) When might you want to use <u>non-Standard English</u> in a story?

....

....   1 mark

I scored ⬜ out of 10.

© CGP — not to be photocopied

End of Grammar Quiz

End of Sentence Punctuation

Remember — sentences should always start with a capital letter.
They can end with a full stop, a question mark or an exclamation mark.

You should avoid writing very long sentences with lots of conjunctions.
A smaller number of shorter sentences is often easier to read.

1 Improve the passage below by splitting it into shorter sentences. You will
need to remove some of the conjunctions and change some punctuation.

From outside the stone walls of the
castle came ghostly shrieks and Bea
and her dog Bouncer quivered in
terror at the thought of what might
be waiting but then, without warning,
came silence and this was even worse.

....

....

....

....

....

2 Explain why this passage is more effective when split into shorter sentences.
Think about how you would want the reader to feel when reading the passage.

....

....

....

If you miss out the punctuation between two sentences, it can be hard to know where the first sentence was meant to end.

My dad told us to go outside and play in the pond we saw a frog and a newt. ✗

In this sentence, it's not clear where Dad told them to play.

3 **Rewrite the sentences below with the <u>correct punctuation</u>.**

Could you move the road isn't wide enough for two cars.

....

....

....

The decorator made a mess when painting pedestrians were told to avoid the wet paint.

....

....

....

4 **Explain what the sentence below means, as it stands.**
How would you change the punctuation so it <u>makes sense</u>?

Straight after lunch, we washed up my grandparents like shiny plates.

....

....

....

....

How well can you use sentence punctuation to make writing clear and easy to read? Tick a box.

Parenthesis

A parenthesis is an extra bit of information added to a sentence.
Usually you use commas to show parenthesis:

> Their two children, a girl and a boy, have birthdays in July.

If the extra information is not very important, you can use a set of
brackets or dashes:

> The medals (two silvers and a bronze) were displayed in a museum.

> He had been an actor — mainly light comedy roles — for ten years.

Whatever punctuation you use, the sentence should still make sense
if the parenthesis is removed.

---

1   Match each <u>numbered sentence</u> to a <u>parenthesis</u> on the right. Write each
sentence out with the parenthesis placed between commas, dashes or brackets.

1. Elephants live in Asia and Africa.

2. My singing performance was a disaster.

3. I pulled out Granny's gift and tried to look grateful.

the orange jumper

filmed by Dad

the largest land mammals

....

....

....

....

....

....

2 Create your own sentences which <u>include the parenthesis</u> given.

(a country in South America)

....

....

— we were never sure who —

....

....

, my best friend,

....

....

(not the one on the table)

....

....

3 Write a <u>suitable parenthesis</u> for each sentence.

The professor, ... ,
threw the equipment across the laboratory and howled in rage.

The money we raised — .... —
was enough to buy a card and a large bunch of flowers.

Both of the countries (....)
have long coastlines.

4 Explain why the <u>brackets</u> in the following sentence have <u>not been used properly</u>.

The training (and equipment) were both excellent.

....

....

How did you find using commas, brackets and dashes to show parenthesis? Tick a box.

☺ ✓   ☺ ✓   ☺ ✓

48

Abbreviations

Proper nouns that are abbreviated still need a capital letter.

Dr ⟵ short form of Doctor

UK ⟵ United Kingdom

Abbreviations that consist of just the first part of the noun will need a full stop.

cent. ⟵ century

Feb. ⟵ February

---

1 Fill in the table to show the **full length** or **abbreviated** form of the words.

Full length word / words	Abbreviation
Mister	....
....	GB
Professor	....
minimum and maximum	.... and ....
kilometre	....
.... or	St
....	Sept.
miles per hour	....
....	NYC
....	tsp

How did you find these abbreviations? Tick a box.

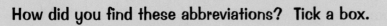

Commas Around Embedded Clauses

A relative clause can be placed within a main clause with commas around it. This makes it an embedded clause.

My dog, who follows me everywhere, chased the cat away.

main clause

1 Match up the <u>main and subordinate clauses</u> and write them out as <u>one sentence</u> containing an <u>embedded clause</u>.

1. Cumbria has many mountains and lakes.

2. Bob decided he would try baking a cake.

3. My sister wants to learn how to drive.

who is nearly 17

where my friend lives

who is a terrible cook

....

....

....

....

....

....

How did you find using embedded clauses? Tick a box.   ✓   ✓   ✓

Commas with Co-ordinating Conjunctions

When you use co-ordinating conjunctions like 'and', 'but', 'so', 'yet' and 'or' to join main clauses, you should put a comma before the conjunction.

> We drove all the way to Cardiff, but the match was in Edinburgh.

main clause   comma and co-ordinating conjunction   main clause

You don't need a comma if what comes after the co-ordinating conjunction is not a complete main clause.

> I explored the woods and found a badger's sett.

No comma, because this is not a complete main clause.
(A main clause makes sense on its own as a sentence.)

---

1 Match each main clause on the left with a main clause on the right. Then write them as <u>one sentence</u>, joined with a <u>comma</u> and a <u>co-ordinating conjunction</u>.

1. My phone's battery is flat

2. Annie's dog looks fierce

3. We could go for a pizza

he's actually a big softy.

we could have a burger.

we'll have to use yours.

....

....

....

....

....

....

2 Add a comma before the conjunction <u>if it is needed</u>.

I dropped the glass but didn't break it.

The squirrel forgot where the acorn was buried so in the spring a tree grew.

Sally had to cross the muddy field yet she arrived with a smile.

The leisure centre has a swimming pool and a hall for indoor sports.

Una entered her drawing into the competition and later she received a letter saying she had won.

3 Write a <u>poem</u> in the template below. Make sure you <u>punctuate</u> each line correctly, with commas where necessary. Give your poem a <u>title</u>.

Title: ....

.... but the wind still blows.

....and the fog still hangs.

.... so the rain still falls.

.... yet the Sun still shines.

.... but ....

.... and ....

.... so ....

.... yet ....

How did you find using commas with co-ordinating conjunctions? Tick a box.

Section 7 — Commas and Apostrophes

Commas to Avoid Confusion

Commas **often help to make the** meaning of a sentence clear.

Help, a snake!

Imagine this sentence
without the comma.

Outside the school buses waited.

Without commas it's impossible to
know where the fronted adverbial ends.

1 Add the <u>missing</u> comma or commas to make these sentences <u>less confusing</u>.

While painting children should take extra care.

All winter animals took shelter from the snow.

In the room above the waiters served the food.

Tomorrow at four twenty guests will arrive.

2 <u>Explain how</u> the comma or commas <u>change the meaning</u> of these sentences.

No kindness is good. ➡ No, kindness is good.

....

....

The teenager thought Arthur should have carried the old man's shopping.

The teenager, thought Arthur, should have carried the old man's shopping.

....

....

She liked Henry, who played rugby better than Daniel.

She liked Henry, who played rugby, better than Daniel.

....

....

In lists, there's usually no comma before the word 'and.'
It's best to add a comma though if the sentence would be confusing without one.

> They ate cheese, eggs, green apples and grapes.

Does this means the apples and the grapes were green?

> They ate cheese, eggs, green apples, and grapes.

Here it's clear that only the apples were green.

3 For each pair of sentences below, **tick** which you think is **better punctuated**, and **explain** your reasoning in the box below.

My heroes are my parents, Mo Farah and Queen Elizabeth. ☐

My heroes are my parents, Mo Farah, and Queen Elizabeth. ☐

We ate onion soup, spicy chicken and mango ice cream. ☐

We ate onion soup, spicy chicken, and mango ice cream. ☐

In the park we saw two squirrels, Mr Smith, and Dr Sidhu. ☐

In the park we saw two squirrels, Mr Smith and Dr Sidhu. ☐

How did you find using commas to avoid confusion? Tick a box.

Commas Between Adjectives

To decide if you need a comma between your adjectives, try putting 'and' between them. If the sentence sounds right with 'and', it needs a comma.

a slow and tedious film ✓ ⟹ Sounds right — needs comma. ⟹ a slow, tedious film

a large and wooden bowl ✗ ⟹ Doesn't sound right — no comma needed. ⟹ a large wooden bowl

1 Add a comma to these noun phrases if it is necessary. Put a tick in the box next to any noun phrases that are already correct.

Arthur wore his stylish waterproof coat. ☐

She was told to expect an amusing handsome man. ☐

Threatening red clouds hung over the factory. ☐

He took shelter from the biting easterly wind. ☐

2 Use two adjectives from the box to turn each noun into a noun phrase. Add your own determiner, and use commas where necessary.

spotted   polar   ripe   tasteless
juicy   enormous   lumpy   colourful

tomato: ....

sweater: ....

custard: ....

bear: ....

How well do you know when to use commas between adjectives? Tick a box.

Punctuating Interjections

Interjections (words like 'ah', 'wow' and 'ouch') can be followed by a comma or an exclamation mark.

| Oh, who did that? | | Oh! Who did that? |

Using an exclamation mark makes the interjection more dramatic.

'Yes', 'No' and people's names work in the same way.

| No, my picture didn't win the contest. | | Ryan! I've got your phone. |

1 Put a **tick** in the box if the sentence is correctly punctuated, put a **cross** if it is **incorrectly** punctuated, and put a **question mark** if you **can't tell**.

Well, that was a lovely meal. ☐

'Wow', is a word that is spelt the same backwards. ☐

Oh, I think I've lost my glasses. ☐

No, dogs were allowed on the field. ☐

Isla, can't help us because she's visiting her gran. ☐

2 Write your own examples of where you would use a **comma** and an **exclamation mark** after an interjection, and explain what is different about them.

[,] ....

[!] ....

The difference is that ....

....

How well do you know when to use a comma or an exclamation mark after an interjection? Tick a box. ☺✓ ☺✓ ☺✓

© CGP — not to be photocopied

Commas for Places and Dates

Places and dates sometimes need commas to separate the different parts.

> My address is 5 Cedar Road, Dover, Kent.

> Her date of birth is 22nd June, 1998.

You don't need a comma when a date is just a month and a year, e.g. 'I went there in August 2016'.

Remember that you also need a comma after a fronted adverbial:

> On 31st January, 2018, there was a spectacular lunar eclipse.

1 Add <u>commas</u> to the following sentences.

The concert was held on 24th August 2016.

On Princes Street Edinburgh there is a large art gallery.

In the summer of 2012 the Olympic Games were held in London England.

2 The sentence below <u>doesn't start</u> with a <u>fronted adverbial</u>, yet there is still a comma after 'London'. Explain how this comma helps to <u>keep the meaning clear</u>.

> 10 Downing Street, London, is the home of the Prime Minister.

....

....

3 Write your own sentence which has a <u>fronted adverbial</u> that includes a <u>date</u>.

....

....

How did you find using commas with places and dates, and after fronted adverbials? Tick a box.

Apostrophes

Apostrophes are used for single possession, plural possession and contraction.

At James's school, the teachers' car park isn't very big.

Single possession —
'the school of James'

Plural possession —
'the car park of the teachers'

Contraction
of 'is not'

1 Add any <u>apostrophes</u> which are missing in the sentences below.

Whose job is it to feed Amys hamster while shes away? Its hungry.

We heard lots of boys and girls singing Christmas carols.

We werent ready for the start of the race, and the girls team beat us easily.

In the players changing room, the goalkeepers shirt was on a bench.

2 Use apostrophes for <u>contraction</u> and <u>possession</u> to <u>shorten</u> these sentences.

I will not help you hide the coat of Dana; it is not a nice thing to do.

....

Who is the man taking the bone of the dogs away?

....

I am not going to clear up the mess of Sarah and Kate.

....

I will not eat the cake of Miles.

....

How did you find using apostrophes? Tick a box.

Section 7 — Commas and Apostrophes

Homophones involving Apostrophes

In some pairs of homophones, one word has an apostrophe and the other doesn't. The word <u>with</u> the apostrophe is usually a contraction, not a possessive.

> Homophones are words that are spelt differently but sound exactly the same.

you're

This is a contraction of 'you are'. ('Your' means 'belonging to you'.)

it's

This is a contraction of 'it is'. ('Its' means 'belonging to it'.)

1 Fill in the gaps in the sentences below with the <u>correct homophone</u>.

[your/you're] Does .... mum know .... staying late?

[whose/who's] .... to know .... coat this is?

[their/they're] .... not unveiling .... new car yet.

[it's/its] Look, ... licking .... paws.

[their/they're] They've rung to say .... on .... way.

2 Write your own sentences using the <u>words in brackets</u> below.

[your] ....

[you're] ....

[theirs] ....

[whose] ....

[its] ....

How did you find using homophones involving apostrophes? Tick a box.

Apostrophes – Tricky Plurals

When nouns are in the plural, sometimes it's hard to know whether they are also a possessive.

My cousin is three years' old.

Is this apostrophe needed?

If you're not sure if it needs an apostrophe, try putting it into the singular.

My cousin is one year old.

It's 'one year old' (not 'one year's old') so it's not a possessive. Therefore 'three years old' does not need an apostrophe.

When the plural of a noun doesn't end in an 's', any 's' at the end must be a possessive. The apostrophe must come before the 's'.

children's clothing

This must be a possessive, as 'children' is already a plural. The apostrophe comes before the 's' — otherwise it would mean 'belonging to the childrens').

1 Add any **apostrophes** which are missing from the sentences below.

In three days time, I will be seeing my cousins again.

Belinda is eight months pregnant.

The bus arrived ten minutes late.

This candidate has five years experience in computer programming.

Our team has won this competition four years running.

2 Correct the phrases below where apostrophes are **missing** or **not used properly**.

mens' toilets   no mans land   the womens faces

the mouse's tail   sheeps wool   people's noses

How did you find using apostrophes with tricky plurals? Tick a box.

Section 8 — Punctuation for Speech

Punctuating Speech

A correctly punctuated direct speech sentence looks like this:

All the words spoken are inside inverted commas.

The reporting clause is outside the inverted commas.

"I don't know why the washing machine isn't working," Jared said to his mother, rocking the old machine gently to and fro, "but I did put the dog's bed in it — and it only just fitted."

There can be punctuation (such as a dash) inside direct speech.

You need commas before and after the reporting clause when it's breaking up a sentence of dialogue.

---

(1) Add a <u>properly punctuated reporting clause</u> and an <u>adverb</u> to the direct speech. You don't have to use 'said' — you can use other verbs of speech.

....

.... "There are some very dark clouds in that sky."

"Hurry up," ....

.... "We're going to be late."

---

(2) Add <u>direct speech</u>, <u>adverbs</u>, <u>phrases</u> or <u>clauses</u> to the reporting clause below to make an <u>exciting piece of writing</u>. Remember to use punctuation correctly.

Your reporting clause is: screamed Sayid and Jamala

....

....

....

---

3 Rewrite these sentences, adding in the <u>correct speech punctuation</u>.

I've no idea where we're going moaned Adam I keep tripping over.

....

....

Monty yelled if you don't hurry up, Bella will have eaten all the cake.

....

....

Isn't it a beautiful sunset Mum said to me as we got out of the car.

....

....

Hey be careful said Sara patting the trembling little dog can't you see that

he's really scared and nervous? ....

....

....

4 This speech sentence is <u>punctuated incorrectly</u>. Write it out correctly.

When I went to my new school I really hated it", Admitted Lily "wiping

away tears" "and each time my teacher opened the door I ran away".

....

....

....

5   **Answer the questions below about what <u>punctuation in direct speech</u> does.**

What are inverted commas for? ....

....

What is a reporting clause? ....

....

6   **The passage below has a lot of <u>punctuation missing</u>. Rewrite it with all the punctuation added, including the <u>speech punctuation</u> and any <u>capital letters</u>.**

> look over there shouted maia pointing to the top of the tree I'm
> sure that's a dinosaur I just saw
> don't be ridiculous replied her mum rolling her eyes crossly there
> are no dinosaurs living today they all died out millions of years ago
> no they didn't maia argued opening her book and showing her
> mum a brightly-coloured picture they just evolved into birds

....

....

....

....

....

....

....

....

....

How did you find punctuating speech? Tick a box.   🙁 ✓   😐 ✓   🙂 ✓

63

Reported Speech to Direct Speech

Reported speech **tells you** what someone said **and** doesn't use inverted commas. When you change reported speech into direct speech, you may need to change the tense of the verb, and shift from the third person to the first person.

Reported speech: | Angelina told me that <u>she was</u> competing in the race.

Direct speech: | Angelina said, "<u>I am</u> competing in the race."

In this example, 'she was' (third person, simple past tense) has changed to 'I am' (first person, simple present tense).

1) Change the passage below from <u>reported</u> to <u>direct</u> speech using correct punctuation, then continue the conversation with <u>more direct speech</u>.

Kai told Rhiann that he was a bit annoyed with her. Rhiann asked him why he was annoyed and what had she done. Kai told her that his bike was old and rusty, and he wished she'd remembered to bring it in out of the rain.

Remember that you use a new line each time a new person speaks.

....

....

....

....

....

....

....

Are you able to change reported speech to direct speech, and punctuate it correctly? Tick a box.

© CGP — not to be photocopied

Section 8 — Punctuation for Speech

Direct Speech to Reported Speech

To change direct to reported speech, you need to be clear who is talking to whom.

"Anna, the weather will be very bad tomorrow," said Pedro.

Here it's Pedro talking to Anna.

To change this to reported speech you could write:

Pedro told Anna that the weather would be very bad the following day.

You could say 'Pedro said to Anna that...,' or 'Pedro mentioned to Anna that...,' or 'Anna was told by Pedro that...' instead.

You then need to change the tense ('will' to 'would'). You may also need to change some of the words so it all makes sense ('tomorrow' to 'the following day').

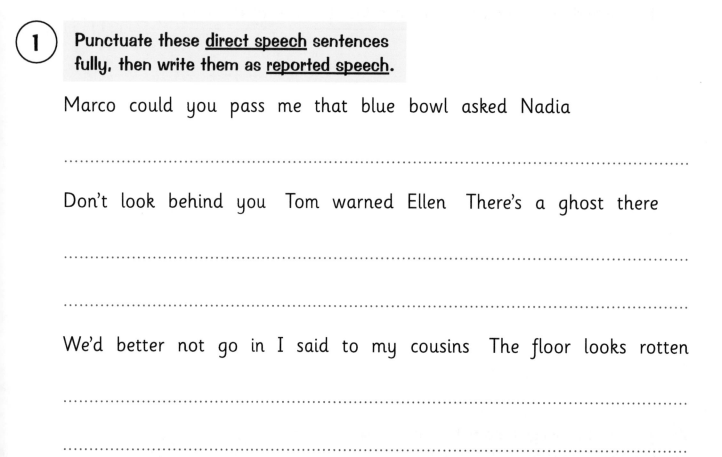

1 Punctuate these <u>direct speech</u> sentences fully, then write them as <u>reported speech</u>.

Marco could you pass me that blue bowl asked Nadia

....

Don't look behind you Tom warned Ellen There's a ghost there

....

....

We'd better not go in I said to my cousins The floor looks rotten

....

....

2 The sentences below have been changed from <u>direct speech to reported speech</u>, but they're not right. Rewrite them as <u>correct reported speech</u>.

Direct: "Oh do hurry up," called Dad, "or there'll be nowhere to park."

Reported: Dad told us to "Hurry up" or there will be nowhere to park. ✘

Correction: ....

....

Direct: "I went to football last night and I broke my ankle," said Joe.

Reported: Joe told me I have gone to football and broken my ankle. ✘

Correction: ....

....

Direct: Eve said, "The history homework was really hard last week."

Reported: "The history homework was really hard last week." told Eve. ✘

Corrected: ....

....

3 Write two sentences of your own in <u>direct</u> and <u>reported</u> speech.

Direct: ....

Reported: ....

Direct: ....

Reported: ....

Were you able to change direct speech to reported speech and correct it if it was wrong? Tick a box. 😕 ☑ 🙂 ☑ 😊 ☑

Paragraph Structure

Sentences within a paragraph should flow logically, otherwise your reader will find it hard to follow what you're trying to say.

The paragraph below is muddled up...

In the museum at Caerleon, we dressed up as Romans, but the clothes were scratchy. When we got there we had to go through the baths and the museum before the shop. We went to see Roman items as we were studying the Romans at school. I sat with Leanne on the coach and Liam was behind us. He kept annoying me by kicking my seat. A guide took us through the museum and showed us all the things.

This sentence is not in the right order of what happened, so it's confusing.

This sentence doesn't fit in at all, because it's about the coach journey.

1 Rewrite the paragraph about the Roman museum trip. Take out the information that <u>shouldn't be there</u>, and put the other information in a <u>better order</u>. You may also want to change words or add words or information.

....

....

....

....

....

....

....

2 Write <u>three paragraphs</u> of information about the <u>last school trip</u> you went on. Make sure you don't muddle information in your paragraphs.

....
....
....
....
....
....
....
....
....
....
....
....

3 Explain your <u>reasoning</u> for how you ordered the information in your paragraphs in Question 2.

....
....
....

How did you find writing paragraphs? Tick a box.

Paragraphs: New Speaker, New Line

When a new person speaks in a dialogue, you need to put the speech on a new line, so it's clear who is speaking. This can be useful because it means you don't need to use a reporting clause every time.

"Don't go in the water," yelled Dan, urgently. "It isn't safe!"
    "Of course it is," replied Ella. "Don't be so silly. Come on!"
    "I don't want to: those waves are huge. I don't want to drown."
    "You'll be fine!"
    "I can't swim in that, Ella!"

← Dan speaks first.

← Ella replies on a new line.

← Although there's no reporting clause, we know this is Dan again because it's on a new line.

← Ella's speech is on a new line.

← Dan is speaking again.

1 Use the 'new paragraph' mark (//) to show where the dialogue should be put on a __new line__. The first one has been done for you.

Example: "Don't do it!" I yelled.//"Don't do what?" she asked, innocently.

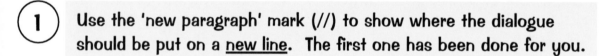

"I'm a bit fed up," I admitted, "actually." "Oh dear, why is that, then?"

"The last time I was in a school play, the scenery fell down on top of the choir." "That sounds exciting, but was anyone hurt?" "No!"

"We need to be careful," explained the wizard, "as the next part of our journey is both difficult and dangerous." "Will we meet any pixies?" asked Robin. "I don't know — we might do. They won't harm us if we sing to them as we pass them." "Oh. It's a shame I can't sing then."

2 <u>Rewrite</u> then <u>continue</u> the dialogue below. Make it clear who is speaking by using a <u>new line</u> for each new speaker, and add <u>reporting clauses</u> where needed.

"Let's make a cake for Mum's birthday," suggested Svenya. "Last time we did it there were eggs all over the floor," mused Natalie, "and she was furious when she came home." "But we're older now and we won't make a mess."

....

....

....

....

....

....

....

....

....

....

....

....

Do you understand the 'new speaker, new line' rule for writing dialogue? Tick a box.

End of Punctuation Quiz

(1) **Punctuate the sentence below to <u>show the parenthesis</u>.**

The prizes silver cups, medals and shields were displayed on a shelf in her bedroom.

(2) **Place <u>commas</u> in the sentence below to make its <u>meaning clear</u>.**

Since Bindi hated tidying more than she hated mess it fell to Mari who was always incredibly tidy to do it for her.

(3) **Rewrite the sentences below. Add any <u>missing apostrophes</u> and change any <u>incorrect spellings</u>.**

Their not feeding the goat. Your feeding it, since its yours.

....

....

(4) **Rewrite this sentence and remove any <u>unnecessary apostrophes</u>.**

The cabbage's and leek's in the grocer's shop we're fresh.

....

....

(5) **Rewrite this <u>direct speech sentence</u> with <u>full, correct punctuation</u>.**

i don't know what you think youre doing with my chain said the ghost but its my job to rattle it

....

....

6 Tick the sentence <u>in each pair</u> which is <u>correctly punctuated</u>.

I opened the fridge, but couldn't find any milk. ☐

I opened the fridge but couldn't find any milk. ☐

The school had new computers and teachers made the most of them. ☐

The school had new computers, and teachers made the most of them. ☐

As soon as he arrived at the fair, he saw all his friends. ☐

As soon as he arrived at the fair he saw all his friends. ☐

☐ 1 mark

7 Explain what is wrong with the <u>layout</u> of this dialogue.

'Where've you been?" said Mo. "In the attic," said Jim, "with the spiders and mice." "Sounds like fun," she replied, dryly.

....

.... ☐ 1 mark

8 Write a <u>direct speech sentence</u> using the words '<u>thanks</u>' and '<u>gulped</u>'.

....

.... ☐ 2 marks

I scored ☐ out of 10.

😟 ✓   🙂 ✓   😃 ✓

End of Punctuation Quiz

Section 10 — Prefixes

Number Prefixes from Latin

Knowing number prefixes can help you to make sense of unfamiliar words. These number prefixes all come from the Latin language.

1 ⇨ unicycle	4 ⇨ quad bike	100 ⇨ century
2 ⇨ bicycle	8 ⇨ octopus	1000 ⇨ millennium
3 ⇨ tricycle	10 ⇨ decade	many ⇨ multiply

1 Circle the **correct answer** to each question.

How many years has an octogenarian lived?   50   80   100

How many sides does a quadrangle have?   4   6   10

How many people make a unilateral decision?   1   10   Many

2 Fill in the gaps to spell a word that **matches each definition**.

Doing many things at once. ☐☐☐☐ t ☐☐☐☐☐ i ☐ g

The hundredth anniversary of something. ☐☐☐ n ☐☐ n ☐☐ y

A series of three books or films. ☐☐☐☐ l ☐ g ☐

3 Draw lines to **match the pictures** to the **labels** and then complete the sentence.

(biped)   (quadruped)   (centipede)

I think the Latin root 'ped(e)' means ....

Prefixes: 'mini' and 'micro'

The prefixes 'mini-' and 'micro-' both mean small.

> The students travelled to York in a minicab.

> The microchips in Bill's phone were frazzled by the spilt water.

1 Write the __prefix__ '__mini-__' or '__micro-__' before the words in the box below. Then write the correct words in the gaps to __complete the sentences__.

> ....organisms ....scope .... bus
>
> ....skirt ....wave ....phone

The .... was unnecessary — everyone could hear Asha's voice without it.

We cooked the popcorn in the ....

.... can be responsible for causing sickness.

The .... was a little tight around the waist.

Under the .... , we could see the tiny insect's antennae.

Our teacher drove us in a .... to the match.

2 Write sentences that use each of the '__mini-__' words below. Use a dictionary to help with any words you don't know.

miniature: ....

minimise: ....

minimum: ....

miniscule: ....

Prefixes: 'bene' and 'mal'

The prefix 'bene-' means good and 'mal-' means bad.
They both come from the Latin language.

benevolence

This means 'good will'.

malevolence

This means 'ill will'.

1 Unscramble the words and draw lines to match them to the correct definitions.

a i m l a r a

....

f i n b e e t

....

a l i o n t r i m n u t

....

f r o a m m e l d

....

f a b e n c r o t e

....

Illness caused by a lack of good food

Something that is poorly shaped

Someone who offers assistance or charity

A deadly disease which is spread by mosquitoes

Advantage taken from something

2 Characters called 'Benvolio' and 'Malvolio' appear in plays by William Shakespeare. Explain how their names might give a clue to the audience about what these characters are like.

....

....

Prefixes: 'ultra' and 'hyper'

The prefix 'ultra-' means 'beyond' or 'extremely'.

In his ultramodern apartment, the carpet was cleaned by a robot.

The prefix 'hyper-' means 'over' or 'greater than normal'.

Jean didn't like it, but she is always hypercritical.

1 Complete the sentences using the **correct words** in the box.

Look the words up in a dictionary if you don't know what they mean.

hypersensitive   ultramarine   hyperspace   ultrasonic

The .... colour of her dress was very eye-catching.

Bats make an .... click that humans struggle to hear.

I was .... to the pollen and started to sneeze immediately.

The captain pressed a button to send the rocket into ....

2 Circle the **correct word** from the **underlined pairs** for each sentence.

The nurse used an ultrasound / hypersound machine to show
the pregnant woman her baby.

My ultra-active / hyperactive hamster keeps running in circles.

Insects can see ultraviolet / hyperviolet light.

3 'Hypothermia' means that your body temperature is <u>too cold</u>.
What do you think that hyperthermia means?

Hyperthermia means ....

....

Prefix: 'fore'

The prefix 'fore-' means 'before' or 'at the front'.

The novel contained a foreword written by another author.

If a book contains a foreword, it will come before the main part of the story.

1 Complete the paragraph below using words that contain the '<u>fore-</u>' prefix.

Many years ago, when our .... moved to this land, it

was .... that one day a hero would be born. The people

would recognise him by a scar on his .... just above his

eyebrows, and an unusually short .... on his left hand.

2 Write your own sentences using the <u>words in boxes</u>.

Use a dictionary if you're not familiar with the word.

(forearm (noun)) ....

....

(forearm (verb)) ....

3 Write down what you think the <u>adage</u> below means, then give a <u>situation</u> in which you could use it.

An adage is a saying that expresses a general truth.

('Forewarned is forearmed.')

I think this adage means ....

....

A situation in which this could be used is ....

....

....

Suffixes: Changing to Verbs

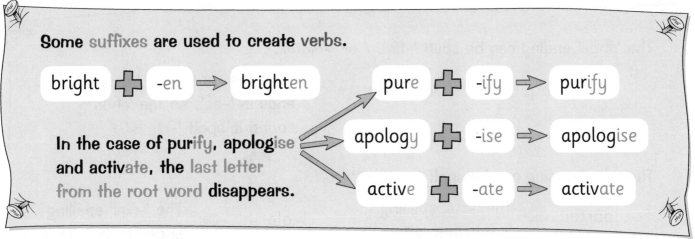

Some suffixes are used to create verbs.

bright ➕ -en ⟹ brighten

In the case of purify, apologise and activate, the last letter from the root word disappears.

pure ➕ -ify ⟹ purify

apology ➕ -ise ⟹ apologise

active ➕ -ate ⟹ activate

1 Create verbs from the words below by adding the correct suffix, then write them in the correct column of the table.

light glory real hard sad simple assassin fright horror ample
captive wide hospital motive active author computer dark
equal note medic straight elastic class just décor advert

-en	-ify	-ise	-ate

2 Choose two verbs you created in Question 1 and use them to write a sentence.

....

....

Suffixes: the Sounds of 'shus' and 'shul'

The 'shus' ending can be spelt '-tious' or '-cious'.

cautious   gracious   ← Here the root word ('grace') ends in '-ce', so the 'shus' sound is spelt '-cious'.

The 'shul' ending can be spelt '-tial' or '-cial'.

partial ← The '-tial' spelling is common after a consonant.

glacial ← The '-cial' spelling is common after a vowel.

There are some exceptions that need to be learned though, e.g. 'initial', 'spatial'.

1 Circle the **correct spelling** of each word in the tables below.

-cious	-tious
delicious	delitious
nutricious	nutritious
vicious	vitious
ambicious	ambitious
caucious	cautious
suspicious	suspitious
conscious	constious
consciencious	conscientious
precious	pretious
supersticious	superstitious
malicious	malitious

-cial	-tial
facial	fatial
special	spetial
inicial	initial
potencial	potential
essencial	essential
financial	finantial
beneficial	benefitial
confidencial	confidential
artificial	artifitial
residencial	residential
commercial	commertial

2 Choose <u>five words</u> from <u>Question 1</u> and write a sentence using each one.

1. My friend made me a delicious cake for my birthday.

2. ....

3. ....

4. ....

5. ....

6. ....

3 Write the word from Question 1 that <u>matches each sentence or definition</u> below. Make sure you spell it correctly.

Something you really need is ....

This is to do with where you live. ....

Someone who really wants to be successful is ....

Someone who won't walk under a ladder is ....

This is to do with money. ....

Someone who always does their duty ....

4 For each <u>adjective</u> below, write down a noun that comes from the same <u>root word</u>.

ferocious ....ferocity........   official ....

atrocious ....   commercial ....

suspicious ....   confidential ....

beneficial ....   essential ....

Suffixes: 'ant', 'ent' and their variants

Some words end in '-ant', and some in '-ent', and it's often hard to know which is the right one to use. Sometimes, thinking about the other word endings for the root word will give you a clue.

If a word has a form with '-ation', it will use '-ant', '-ance' and '-ancy'.

observation   observant

If a word has a form with '-ential', it will use '-ent', '-ence' and '-ency'.

confidential   confident

These tricks don't work for all words, so some words just have to be learned.

(1) **Fill in** the table with the words ending in '<u>ation</u>' or '<u>ential</u>', and use these to decide on the spelling of the related words ending in '<u>ant</u>' or '<u>ent</u>'.

Root	Related word ending -**ation** or -**ential**	Related word ending -**ant** or -**ent**
inform	information	informant
preside		
vary		
apply		
expect		
reside		
torr-		
jubil-		

2 Use the clues in the sentences below to give the correct spellings of the related <u>nouns</u> ending in '<u>ance</u>' or '<u>ence</u>'. The first one has been done for you.

'Avoid' won't make 'avoidation', but it will make ....*avoidance*.......... .

'Resist' will make 'resistant', and it will also make ....

'Cohere' will make 'coherent', and it will also make ....

'Perform' won't make 'performation', but it will make ....

'Prefer' will make 'preferential', and it will also make ....

3 For each sentence below, put a tick in the box if the <u>underlined words</u> are <u>spelled correctly</u>.

Joe liked to think that he was a very <u>independant</u> person. ☐

"I don't know why you're looking so <u>innocent</u>! You broke it!" ☐

I was <u>hesitent</u> about joining in their game, but I did enjoy myself. ☐

He's such an <u>arrogant</u> person — it's hard to like him, actually. ☐

It was really <u>evidant</u> that Sam hadn't revised for the test at all. ☐

She's quite a <u>tolerent</u> person, but she doesn't like noise. ☐

4 Add '<u>-ant</u>' or '<u>-ent</u>' to the words below so that they are <u>spelled correctly</u>.

obedi...................   instrum...................   developm...................

perman...................   dorm...................   achievem...................

flu...................   anci...................   contest...................

relev...................   signific...................   judgem...................

indiffer...................   extravag...................   triumph...................

Section 11 — Word Endings and Suffixes

5 For each sentence below, circle the underlined word that is spelled correctly.

He's a bad <u>influence</u> / <u>influance</u>: I wish you wouldn't play with him.

There is no <u>difference</u> / <u>differance</u> between our heights.

There's a <u>vacancy</u> / <u>vacency</u> for a part-time teacher in our school.

Quick! Call the ambulance, we've got an <u>emergancy</u> / <u>emergency</u> !

She has a <u>tendancy</u> / <u>tendency</u> to lose her temper over small things.

There needs to be a bit more <u>efficiancy</u> / <u>efficiency</u> around here.

6 Fill in the endings of the words below with either '<u>ance</u>' or '<u>ence</u>'.

I can't see any real evid.................. that aliens have landed on Earth.

She doesn't have much experi.................. , so she's finding it hard.

Lenny was reading a book about artificial intellig.................. .

He will need some guid.................. to be able to carry out that task.

Use the dictionary for refer.................. when you do the homework.

"I have no more pati.................. with your mess," yelled Mum.

7 Write <u>five sentences</u> of your own, including words ending in '<u>ance</u>', '<u>ence</u>', '<u>ancy</u>' or '<u>ency</u>'.

1. ....

2. ....

3. ....

4. ....

5. ....

Words Containing 'ei' and 'ie'

Use this rhyme to help you remember how to spell ei and ie words:

'i' before 'e' except after 'c'

piece   relieve

ceiling   deceive

Exceptions to the rule: seize, protein, species

The above rule only applies when the letters make an 'ee' sound. When they make a different sound, you need to learn the spellings.

weight   scientist

1 Complete each word below by writing '**ie**' or '**ei**' in the gap.

soc.............ty   fr..........nd   consc...........nce   perc...........ved

for..........gn   sc..........nce   effic...........ncy   rec...........ve

conc.........ved   suffic...........nt   l..........sure   rec...........pt

2 Use the **correct words** from **Question 1** to complete these sentences.

I hope to .... the book I ordered by next week.

They .... a plan to solve all the problems.

Only thirty miles to the gallon is quite poor fuel ....

I want to return a dress I bought, but I can't find the ....

Michael .... a change in his father's mood.

3 Write a **sentence** containing as many different '**ie**' and '**ei**' words as you can manage. (Your sentence doesn't need to make much sense.)

I perceive the weight of my friend to be sufficient for his height.

Look back at Question 1 if you're stuck for ideas.

....

....

Words Containing Double Consonants

Some words double their final consonant to keep the vowel sound short when a suffix is added.

kidnapped ✓

kidnaped ✗

Spelled this way, it would sound like 'kid-nay-pt'.

For lots of words though, you need to learn which consonants are single and which are double.

accompany

interruption

1 Draw lines to match the <u>incomplete words</u> to the correct <u>double consonants</u>.

a........arently

co........unity

a........ressively

a........reciate

-cc-

-gg-

-pp-

-mm-

o........upy

i........ediately

a........ording

o........ortunity

2 Use some of the <u>words you created</u> in <u>Question 1</u> to complete these sentences.

The cat hissed .... at the vet.

.... to the map, we have nearly reached our destination.

I .... your hard work and all the help you have given me.

We will put a plaster on your knee at the first .... we get.

If you hear the alarm, ... leave the building.

The scouts met in the .... hall.

.... , it was Zara who told Rob I was scared of spiders.

© CGP — not to be photocopied

3 Add the <u>double consonants</u> to these words and write the <u>full word underneath</u>.

bri........iant	co........espond	reco........end
....	....	....

emba........a........	exa........erate	su........icient
....	....	....

su........estion	co........unicate	co........i........ee
....	....	....

Difficult spellings can be remembered by creating a mnemonic, like this one for the word necessary.

Never Eat Chips Eat Salad Sandwiches And Remain Young

4 Create your own <u>mnemonic</u> for each of the words below.

marvellous ....

....

....

address ....

....

....

excellent ....

....

Silent Letters

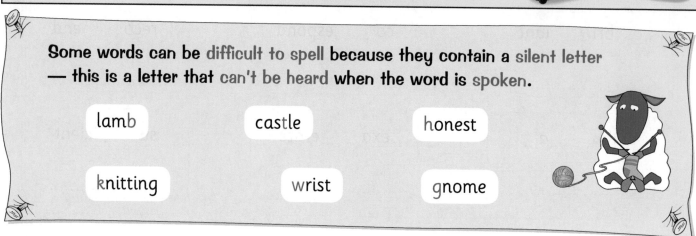

Some words can be difficult to spell because they contain a silent letter — this is a letter that can't be heard when the word is spoken.

lamb   castle   honest

knitting   wrist   gnome

1 Add the correct silent letter to each of the words below.

lis......en   dou......t   mec......anic

s......ord   autum......   ......sychology

desi......n   fas......inate   r......ythm

2 Solve the clues and write your answers in the boxes. Each word contains a silent letter. Find the hidden message in the coloured boxes.

phantom — 1 [ ][ ][ ][s][t]

bit of butter — 2 [n][ ][b]

money borrowed to buy a house — 3 [m][ ][ ][g][ ][ ]

follower of Jesus — 4 [ ][i][ ][ ][i][ ][l][ ]

reply to a question — 5 [a][ ][ ][ ][ ]

furniture used for storage — 6 [ ][ ][p][ ][ ][ ][d][ ]

squirm — 7 [ ][ ][ ][g][g][ ][ ]

medieval warrior — 8 [ ][ ][ ][g][ ][t]

hidden message: ....

The Many Sounds of 'ough'

The 'ough' letter string can be hard to identify in a word because it can make many different sounds.

'ough' sounds like 'off'...   ... or like 'or'...   ... or like 'oh'.

cough   bought   dough

1 Draw <u>lines</u> between the pairs of words that have the <u>same 'ough' sound</u>.

nought   thorough   bough

plough   trough

cough   brought   borough

2 Write a word containing '<u>ough</u>' that <u>rhymes</u> with the word in each box.

scruff
....

slow
....

true
....

scout
....

sport
....

3 Write a sentence of your own containing as many <u>different pronunciations</u> of '<u>ough</u>' as you can manage. (Your sentence doesn't need to make much sense!)

Although there are many ploughs in this borough, there aren't enough troughs.

....

....

....

Section 12 — Confusing Words

88

End of Spelling Quiz

1 Put these number prefixes in <u>numerical order</u> (low to high).

dec oct cent bi mille tri uni

.... ➡ .... ➡ .... ➡ .... ➡ .... ➡ .... ➡ ....

☐ 1 mark

2 Find a word with the prefix '<u>mini</u>' or '<u>micro</u>' that matches these definitions.

A small version of a larger object: ....

A tiny component inside a computer: ....

☐ 1 mark

3 Complete the sentences below to show you understand the <u>meaning</u> of the <u>underlined words</u>.

A <u>beneficial</u> diet is one that ....

A <u>maleficent</u> person ....

☐ 1 mark

4 Underline the word in <u>bold</u> which is the <u>correct word</u> for each sentence.

They scanned his heart using **hypersound / ultrasound**.

Hypertension / ultratension is 'high blood pressure'.

☐ 1 mark

5 Add '<u>-en</u>', '<u>-ify</u>', '<u>-ise</u>' or '<u>-ate</u>' to turn these words into <u>verbs</u>. You may have to <u>add</u>, <u>remove</u> or <u>change</u> letters in the <u>root word</u>.

electric ....   dark ....

medicine ....   apology ....

identity ....   threat ....

☐ 1 mark

End of Spelling Quiz

© CGP — not to be photocopied

6 Correct the spelling of these <u>incorrectly spelled words</u>.

inicial   pretious   spetial   gratious

....   1 mark

7 Write out the correct forms of the words below ending in '<u>ant</u>' or '<u>ent</u>'.

observe   confide   cohere   expect

....   1 mark

8 Rewrite the sentence below. Check the spelling of the words containing '<u>ei</u>' or '<u>ie</u>' and <u>correct them</u> if they are incorrect.

I percieve he has deceived me about the wieght of the peice of pie!

....

....   1 mark

9 Add the <u>missing silent letters</u> to the words below.

dou_tful   as__ma   _rench   mus_le   _terodactyl   solem_   1 mark

10 Write the <u>word</u> that goes with each <u>cryptic definition</u> below.

Hint: all the words have something in common.

If you've not had this, you may want more. ....

If you're wise, you'll take this with the smooth. ....

You really knead this! ....

These nothings are a game with crosses. ....   1 mark

Ahem! ....

I scored [ ] out of 10.

© CGP — not to be photocopied   End of Spelling Quiz

End of Book Test

1 Write each of the underlined words in the sentence below in the correct box to show whether it is a **preposition**, a **determiner** or a **pronoun**.

"He found his book on that chair by the bed

where he had put it last night," said Emil.

prepositions	determiners	pronouns

1 mark

2 Find an example from the passage of each of the **verb forms** listed below.

Chloe was walking along the road when she found a small, silvery egg. She had never seen one like it before, so she picked it up.

"I have decided to keep it and see if it will hatch," she told her mum.

simple past: ....

past progressive: ....

present perfect: ....

past perfect: ....

1 mark

3 Write a sentence which includes a **modal verb** and the word '**fly**'.

....

....

1 mark

End of Book Test

© CGP — not to be photocopied

4 **Rewrite the passage below so that it's in <u>sentences</u> and has <u>correct punctuation</u>.**

when she was dressed jamila ran downstairs hoping max her friend who was often late would have arrived she and max were going to bens house for his birthday party.

....

....

....

.... 2 marks

5 **Write down the meaning of the prefix '<u>fore</u>'. Then write a sentence which includes <u>a word with this prefix</u>.**

'Fore' means ....

....

.... 1 mark

6 **Rewrite the sentences with the <u>correct apostrophes</u>.**

Ellas dogs naughty. Hes alway's growling at you and its scary.

....

.... 1 mark

7 **Circle the <u>correct spelling</u> of the <u>underlined words</u> in the sentence.**

<u>Inicially</u> / <u>Initially</u> he said the <u>performance</u> / <u>performence</u> was <u>briliant</u> / <u>brilliant</u>, but then he <u>admitted</u> / <u>admited</u> he had <u>exagerated</u> / <u>exaggerated</u>. 1 mark

End of Book Test

8 Add a correctly punctuated <u>fronted adverbial</u> to each of the sentences below. Use one adverbial of <u>time</u> and one of <u>place</u>.

.... the small group of soldiers on

horseback galloped up the hill towards the derelict castle.

.... the fisherman pulled his

nets into the boat and inspected his catch.

1 mark

9 Copy the <u>modal verbs</u> from the passage into one of the boxes below to show whether they express <u>possibility</u> or <u>obligation</u>.

You could try learning the violin if you want to, but you might be better suited to the piano. You may have to try both before deciding on what you like. You should remember that learning an instrument means you must practise every day to improve your skills.

possibility	obligation

1 mark

10 Rewrite the sentence with the <u>extra information</u> below added to the sentence as a <u>parenthesis</u>. You may <u>change the wording</u> to make the sentence <u>flow</u>.

Last night, a bright light shone through my window and woke me.

Extra information: The light was pulsing and glowed deep red.

....

....

....

1 mark

11 Correct the spellings below by adding in the <u>missing silent letters</u>.

nitting ....   clim ....

sutle ....   rusle ....

musle ....   onour ....

1 mark

12 Change the <u>reported speech</u> to <u>direct speech</u> and punctuate it.

Dai told his mum that their dog Rex had dug up all her carrots and was sitting in the garden chewing one.

....

....

....

1 mark

13 Put a tick or cross to show whether the <u>clauses</u> in these sentences are <u>correctly linked</u>.

I was shopping, afterwards I went to the cinema. ☐

She ate lunch and then had a bowl of ice cream. ☐

I kept trying, eventually I caught the ball. ☐

Don't eat sweets now: we're having dinner later. ☐

He got in through the window, luckily he's skinny! ☐

1 mark

14 Change the words below into <u>verbs</u> by adding a <u>suffix</u>.

terror ....   intense ....

length ....   captive ....

1 mark

15 Complete the spellings of the words below. Think of a related word that ends with '<u>ential</u>' or '<u>antial</u>' and write it in the brackets.

resid <u>e</u> nce ⟶ ......residential......

influ__nce ⟶ ....

subst__nce ⟶ ....

ess__nce ⟶ ....

1 mark

16 Write a sentence using each word in the <u>homophone pairs</u> shown below.

you're: ....

your: ....

they're: ....

their: ....

it's: ....

its: ....

3 marks

17 Complete these sentences with the <u>correct type of relative clause</u>.

A relative clause in which the relative pronoun has been missed out:

The train .... was late.

A relative clause which adds extra information:

Tamsin ....

was not a good swimmer but was extremely good at football.

1 mark

End of Book Test   © CGP — not to be photocopied

18 Write a <u>short conversation</u> between Ahmed, who likes science, and Jack, who finds it boring. Remember to use the '<u>new speaker, new line</u>' rule.

....

....

....

....

....

.... 2 marks

19 Rewrite the sentences below as one sentence that includes a <u>conditional clause</u>.

She has to do that test. She might not want to, but she must.

....

The train may be cancelled. We intend to go to the match.

.... 1 mark

20 The sentence below uses <u>phrases and clauses</u> to make it <u>flow smoothly</u>. Give an <u>example</u> of each type of phrase or clause.

Thanks to its many priceless works of art, Florence is an essential holiday destination for anyone who loves history and culture.

A relative clause: ....

A fronted adverbial: .... 2 marks

I scored [ ] out of 25.

Glossary

Adverb — A word that describes a **verb**, an **adjective** or other **adverbs**.

Adverbial — A group of words that behaves like an **adverb**.

Clause — Part of a sentence that contains a **subject** and a **verb**.

Conjunction — A word or phrase that **joins** two parts of a sentence, e.g. I play football <u>and</u> I play tennis.

Determiner — Tells you if a **noun** is **general** or **specific**, e.g. I would like <u>a</u> drink. I would like <u>that</u> drink.

Direct Speech — The **actual words** the speaker says.

Main Clause — A clause that **makes sense** on its own, e.g. <u>We play outside</u> when it is not raining.

Modal Verb — A type of verb showing **certainty**, **ability** or **obligation**, e.g. We <u>must</u> hurry. They <u>might</u> go shopping.

Parenthesis — A piece of **extra information** added to a sentence. The sentence will still make sense if the parenthesis is removed.

Phrase — A group of words usually without a **verb**.

Pronoun — A word used to **replace** a **noun**, e.g. **it**, **we**, **you**.

Relative Clause — A **subordinate clause** that tells you more about a noun. It is often introduced by a **relative pronoun**, e.g. He's the man **<u>who</u>** lives here.

Reported Speech — A **description** of someone's speech.

Subordinate Clause — A clause that **doesn't make sense** on its own, e.g. We play outside <u>when it is not raining</u>.

Glossary

PUNCTUATION MARKS

Apostrophes — show **missing letters** and **possession**.	`'`
Brackets — **separate extra information** in a sentence.	`( )`
Colons — **introduce** some **lists** and **join clauses**.	`:`
Commas — used in **lists**, to **join clauses**, to separate **extra information** and after **fronted adverbials**.	`,`
Dashes — **separate extra information** in a sentence.	`—`
Exclamation marks — show **exclamations**, **commands** or **strong emotions**.	`!`
Hyphens — used to **join words** or **add** a **prefix**.	`-`
Inverted commas — show **direct speech**.	`" "`

VERB FORMS

Simple <u>Past</u> — I <u>ate</u>, you <u>ate</u>, etc.

Simple <u>Present</u> — I <u>eat</u>, you <u>eat</u>, etc.

<u>Past</u> Progressive — I <u>was</u> eating, you <u>were</u> eating, etc.

<u>Present</u> Progressive — I <u>am</u> eating, you <u>are</u> eating, etc.

<u>Past</u> Perfect — I <u>had</u> eaten, you <u>had</u> eaten, etc.

<u>Present</u> Perfect — I <u>have</u> eaten, you <u>have</u> eaten, etc.

Answers

Grammar

Section 1 – Word Classes

Pages 4 and 5 – Nouns – Singular and Plural

1. There are lots of possible answers to this question. Examples:
    The <u>llama</u> chased the (dogs) across the <u>field</u>.
    Make sure you have underlined the singular noun in your answer and circled the plural noun.

2. women, series, calves, loaves, person, crisis, cactus, spacecraft, axes, sheep, criteria, louse, fish, bacterium, deer, index
    Note: The most common plural of 'person' is 'people'. 'Persons' can be used when their individual nature is being emphasised.

3. You should have circled: **furniture, information, bread, help, honesty, fun, advice, gold**

4. Any suitable explanation. Example:
    When used in the singular, the word 'cheese' is an uncountable noun that refers to cheese in general. The countable noun 'cheeses' refers to more than one type of cheese, rather than cheese as a whole.

5. There are lots of possible answers to this question. Example:
    (non-countable) Too much sugar is bad for your health.
    (countable) I take two sugars in my tea.

Page 6 – Verb Agreement

1. You should have circled:
    Emily **eats** cereal every day for breakfast.
    The children **call** loudly to their friends to come and play.
    Seven deer **run** out into the meadow to eat the grass.

2. There are lots of possible answers to this question. Examples:
    Meg and Suki **watch** a film together every Sunday.
    The Sahara Desert **stretches** from the Red Sea to the Atlantic Ocean.

3. There are lots of possible answers to this question. Examples:
    My <u>teacher</u> (takes) the register.
    <u>Everyone</u> (has) lunch in the dining hall.
    The <u>boys</u> (play) tag in the playground.
    Make sure you have circled the verbs in your answers and underlined the nouns that they agree with.

Page 7 – Prepositions, Determiners and Pronouns

1. I went <u>to</u> the seaside <u>for</u> a week.
    Do you know <u>whose</u> books <u>the</u> caretaker found?
    <u>This</u> is my favourite. <u>I</u> like <u>yours</u> too though.

2. There are lots of possible answers to this question. Examples:
    She gave **your** money to Eva.
    I left my money **with** Eva.
    I gave **his notebook** to Eva.

Pages 8 and 9 – Noun or Verb?

1. **cut** is a noun
    match is a noun
    part is a noun
    hug is a verb
    paint is a verb
    bank is a verb
    dress is a noun
    fall is a noun
    excuse is a verb
    guard is a verb

2. There are lots of possible answers to this question.
    light: (noun) There was not enough light to read. (verb) Our torch will light the way.
    order: (noun) Please place your order at the desk. (verb) I didn't order this!
    plant: (noun) There was a lovely plant on the window sill. (verb) We need to plant the bulbs soon.
    stamp: (noun) Do you have a postage stamp? (verb) Don't stamp your feet like that!
    photograph: (noun) He took a photograph with his new camera. (verb) It is forbidden to photograph the paintings.
    water: (noun) I drank a glass of water. (verb) Don't forget to water the garden.

3. There are lots of possible answers to this question. Example:
    She used to **dream** about becoming an astronaut.
    I had a bad **dream** last night.

Page 10 – Determiner or Pronoun?

1. **Those** is a determiner
    This is a pronoun
    his is a pronoun
    Which is a determiner

Answers

2. There are lots of possible answers to this question. Remember that if a word is being used as a determiner, it will come <u>before a noun</u>. If it is a pronoun, it will be <u>doing the job of a noun</u>.
   Examples:
   (determiner) I don't own **many** books.
   (pronoun) There were lots of cakes but I didn't eat **many**.
   (determiner) I find **some** computer games a bit boring.
   (pronoun) **Some** were old, and **some** were new.
   (determiner) Do you have **any** advice for me?
   (pronoun) Sorry, I don't have **any**.

Page 11 — Adjective or Adverb?

1. **weekly** is an **adverb** in this sentence.
   weekly is an **adjective** in this sentence.
   still is an **adjective** in this sentence.
   still is an **adverb** in this sentence.
   straight is an **adjective** in this sentence.
   straight is an **adverb** in this sentence.

2. There are lots of possible answers to this question.
   Examples:
   The butterflies were extremely **pretty**.
   Lucy made some **pretty** mean comments.
   Kai's new board game was very **hard**.
   He hit the ground **hard**.

Section 2 — Verb Forms

Pages 12 and 13 — The Past Perfect

1. She had achieved — past perfect
   You are deciding — present progressive
   He was suggesting — past progressive
   I have persuaded — present perfect
   We interrupted — simple past
   We are recommending — present progressive
   I was accompanying — past progressive
   I have guaranteed — present perfect
   She had recognised — past perfect
   You exaggerated — simple past

2. There are lots of possible answers to this question.
   Examples:
   I have done a lot of sport today. (present perfect)
   At 3 pm I played football. (simple past)
   At 12 noon I had already gone out for a jog. (past perfect)

3. There are lots of possible answers to this question.
   Example:
   Before I had learned to knit, I was envious of people who could. I found learning to knit frustrating at times. Now that I have learned, I make scarves for people. I just hope I will get quicker at it!
   This answer contains the <u>past perfect</u> (had learned), the <u>simple past</u> (was, could, found), the <u>present perfect</u> (have learned) and the <u>simple present</u> (make, hope, will). So 4 verb forms. (The modal verb 'will' shows the future, but it is still a present tense verb form.)

Pages 14 and 15 — Tenses in Written Speech

1. You should have underlined: **called**, **didn't**, **said**, **shouted**, **moaned**, **bought**, **wanted**, **said**, **went**, **were eating**, **said**
   You should have circled: **will be going**, **will you come**, **take**, **will do**, **tidy**, **am**, **haven't had**, **have**, **go**, **will play**, **will sit**, **attack**, **will be**

2. There are lots of possible answers to this question.
   Example:
   Jenny <u>shouted</u>, "Who <u>has eaten</u> my special sandwich which I <u>was saving</u> for later?"
   (There are 3 verb forms in this example.)

3. past progressive: 'were creaking' / 'was screaming'
   simple past: 'blotted out' / 'said' / 'struggled' / 'would'
   simple present: 'is'
   past perfect: 'had known'
   (Other forms you may have given are infinitives ('to open', 'to do' and 'to be'), and present perfect ('have stayed').)

4. Any suitable answer. Example:
   The narrative and the reporting clause are always in the same tense.

5. Any suitable answer. Example:
   You can use a mixture of present and past tense verb forms when a character speaks.

Pages 16 and 17 — Modal Verbs

1. You should have circled: **I would be**, **They might think**, **You may go**, **We could take**, **Would you like**, **She should never**, **We may not**, **I shouldn't**, **We could, perhaps**

2. There are lots of possible answers to this question.
   Example:
   I would like to come to your party but I might not be able to because my uncle may be coming to visit.

Answers

3. There are lots of possible answers to this question. Examples:
    If you swim in that lake, you **might get cold**.
    Ask your mum for some chocolate. She **might give you some**.
    If you tried, I am sure **you would be able to do it**.
    I **wouldn't touch that** if I were you!
    He **would share them with you** if he had any.

4. There are lots of possible answers to this question. Examples:
    I could go shopping, but the shops might be closed.
    Dad may have said I could have sweets.
    We would like to go on holiday, but my mum might not have enough money.
    I mustn't take my bike because it might get stolen.
    Gran said I shouldn't watch TV, but I will watch it anyway.

Pages 18-20 – Verbs to show Character Motivation

1. Two modal verbs: would, might
    past perfect: had realised
    simple present: think, is
    simple past: was, said
    reporting clause verb form: simple past

2. There are lots of possible answers to this question. Examples:
    I <u>was feeling</u> unwell, so I didn't go to school.
    She <u>has thought</u> about what you said.
    We <u>had wanted</u> to go to Rome, but we couldn't afford it.
    I <u>will stop</u> talking to you if you keep being rude to me.

3. Any suitable answer. Examples:
    If she **had seen** them, I am sure she would have stopped.
    Since he **told** me that, I can't think of anything else.
    If I'd known, **I might have been able to help** her.
    Before you go, you **must tidy up** the mess in here.
    If he did it, then he **should own up** to what he did.

4. There are lots of possible answers, e.g.:
    I am not staying here any longer, thought Tam. I **have been** a servant for long enough. It **is** time I **make** (or **made**) my own way in the world. So that night, he **stole** out of the house and **crept** to the boatshed. Even though it **would be** hard to sail the boat, he **knew** it was his only chance. This time he **would** succeed.

5. You should have underlined: **hadn't been, had not had, were, was sawing, parted, didn't have, thought, hauled, got, pushed**
    You should have circled: **would, might, could**

6. <u>had sprung</u> — past perfect
    <u>could</u> — modal verb
    <u>was filling</u> — past progressive
    <u>I'm</u> — present
    <u>it's getting</u> — present progressive
    <u>said</u> — simple past

7. There are lots of possible answers to this question. Make sure yours includes plenty of modal verbs which show Tam's thoughts and feelings.

Section 3 – Phrases and Clauses

Page 21 – Relative Clauses

1. You should have underlined: **which was clearly frightened, who had a terrible cold, that have got wet, whose sister I also know**
    You should have circled: **cat, singer, Rocks, Saba**

2. Any suitable relative clauses. Example:
    Freddie, **who has a pet snake**, lives next door to me.
    The book, **which sounded quite boring at first**, was really good.
    He had never been to Lincoln, **which was where his cousins lived.**

Pages 22 and 23 – More about Relative Clauses

1. The ball <u>that belonged to Hamid</u> was thrown over the fence. **W**
    Joe, <u>who was very tired</u>, fell asleep in the car going home. **E**
    Dogs <u>that are not trained properly</u> can be dangerous. **W**
    Cliffs <u>which are undermined by the sea</u> often collapse. **W**
    Their group, <u>which had been lagging behind the others</u>, got lost. **E**
    Amit, <u>whose dad works on a farm</u>, really loves animals. **E**

2. Any suitable answer. Example:
    The relative clauses containing extra information are separated from the main clause with commas.

3. Any suitable relative clauses. Examples:
    The lady **I met yesterday** was very kind.
    The car **Holly bought** broke down yesterday.

4. Any suitable relative clauses. Examples:
    The holidays, **which had been so fun and relaxing**, were a distant memory.
    The lazy kitten, **which had been out all morning**, quickly fell asleep.

Answers

5. Any suitable explanation of the difference in meaning between the two sentences. Examples:
The first sentence implies that only children who can't read maps may get lost.
The second sentence implies that children may get lost because they can't read maps.

Pages 24 and 25 – Fronted Adverbials

1. After dinner, — time
Forty miles away, — place
Nearly always, — frequency
Due to the heat, — cause
His hands trembling, — manner
Out in the rain, — place
In desperation, — manner
Only occasionally, — frequency
That very morning, — time
For that reason, — cause
Whenever she could, — frequency
Like a panther, — manner

2. Whenever she could, Mel swam in the lake.
Without any warning at all, the bull charged at us.

3. There are lots of possible answers to this question. Examples:
With a feeling of relief, he went on holiday.
Before it had chance to catch them, they ran away.
Halfway up the mountain, she left him behind.
In order to avoid being caught, they ran away.
At least twice a year, he went on holiday.

4. There are lots of possible answers to this question. Example:
After four hours of searching, the walker finally found his lost dog.

Pages 26 and 27 – Fronted Adverbials for Effect

1. There are lots of possible answers to this question. Examples:
Although her feet were blistered, Anna was not in the least bit tired.
With a tiny stub of chalk, I drew on the wall to pass the time.
As soon as their backs were turned, Jamal attacked the kidnappers.
His eyes filling with tears of hope, the sailor exclaimed, 'There it is!'
Sails billowing in the morning breeze, the boat glided into the distance.
With the faintest of sighs, Sara slumped to her knees.

2. There are lots of possible answers to this question. Example:
[chosen adverbial from Question 1 about the boat gliding into the distance]
The adverbial helps the reader to imagine what the boat looked like as it glided into the distance.

3. There are lots of possible answers to this question. Examples:
Although healthy eating may seem boring, **you can still enjoy delicious meals.**
Far from being a waste of time, **the meeting solved a number of problems.**
In spite of their objections, **Larry went to the party.**
However loud you shout, **nobody will listen to you.**

4. There are lots of possible answers to this question. Examples:
Desperate to escape the haunted mansion, he ran for his life.
Although you make a good point, I disagree with you completely.
Her heart pounding in her chest, Sandy hid under the dusty bed.
Whilst most of my friends like Physics, I prefer Maths.

5. There are lots of possible answers to this question. Make sure yours includes two sentences with fronted adverbials to paint a picture and to set up a contrast.

Section 4 – Linking Ideas

Pages 28 and 29 – Linking Ideas with Conditional Clauses

1. You should have put a tick next to the following sentences:
I will go to the fair with you tomorrow if you let me.
Even if it is fine, I won't go with you to the fair tomorrow.
We should go to the fair whether you want to or not.
Provided that the weather is fine, we will go to the fair.
I think we will go to the fair unless the weather is too cold.

2. There are lots of possible answers to this question. Examples:
Unless she starts being nice to me, I have no intention of helping her.
If she agrees to help me, I shall definitely help her.

Answers

3. Any suitable rewriting of the sentences.
   Examples:
   Provided that the car is mended, he will go to the football match.
   So long as you don't get it dirty, you can wear my new scarf.
   Whether she wants to or not, she must go to school.

4. There are lots of possible answers to this question. Make sure yours includes plenty of conditional clauses.

Page 30 – Linking Ideas: Conjunctions and Adverbs

1. You should have ticked:
   He tried several times, and eventually he managed it.
   He tried several times. Eventually, he managed it.
   They decided to have the party outside. Luckily, it stayed dry.
   They decided to have the party outside, and luckily it stayed dry.
   You should have crossed:
   He tried several times, eventually he managed it.
   They decided to have the party outside, luckily it stayed dry.

2. Any suitable linking words. Examples:
   It has been a cold spring, **and consequently** the garden hasn't grown much.
   I expect he will be late **because unfortunately** there have been long delays on that road.

Pages 31 and 32 – Linking Ideas in Fiction Writing

1. In the text you should have underlined the adverbials and subordinate clauses given below.
   5 time adverbials: before, then, after that, that evening, Meanwhile
   4 place adverbials: all around them, in front of their new dwelling, through the surrounding woods, back at the camp
   2 subordinate clauses showing time and place: while Peter sat nearby unpacking the mats and sleeping bags, After washing the plates in the stream a little way off

2. They were watching some seals swimming nearby. — 2
   They couldn't see a thing. — 4
   It was starting to get foggy. — 3
   Jane and Peter decided to go sailing in their new boat. — 1
   Any suitable answer. Example:
   Jane and Peter decided to go sailing in their new boat <u>before dinner</u>. <u>While</u> they were watching some seals swimming nearby, they <u>suddenly</u> noticed that it was starting to get foggy and <u>after a few minutes</u>, they couldn't see a thing.

3. Any suitable time and place links.
   Examples:
   The fog was a white blanket. **On all sides of the boat**, Jane could see walls of cloud. **For what felt like a lifetime**, they just sat, shivering and miserable, and waited. It seemed to take hours, but **eventually** the wind rippled the soft clouds away, and a watery sun shone. **In the distance**, they could see a little island. **Within minutes**, they reached it. **Above their heads**, they saw exotic birds flying **towards the jungle**.

Pages 33-35 – Linking Ideas in Arguments

1. Any suitable answer. Examples:
   Some think homework is a good idea, **while** others don't.
   I dislike maths lessons a lot, **whereas** I like English lessons.
   Mum likes me to do my homework straight away. **Furthermore**, she insists that I do it where she can see I'm actually working.
   Homework helps you to revise what you've learned. **Moreover**, it helps teachers check whether you've understood what they taught you.
   Although some pupils don't enjoy doing homework, it does help them to learn.

2. There are lots of possible answers to this question.
   Example:
   At weekends, I enjoy spending time with my family **as well as** all my friends.

3. There are lots of possible answers to this question.
   Examples:
   For:
   They are useful in emergencies.
   They can be used to check spellings/calculations.
   There are lots of educational apps you can use.
   Against:
   They can cause distractions during lessons.
   People can cheat with their work.
   They often get broken.

Answers

4. There are lots of possible answers to this question. Make sure yours includes two arguments for having mobile phones which are linked together using an addition link.

5. There are lots of possible answers to this question. Make sure yours includes one argument for and one argument against having mobile phones which are linked together using a contrast link.

6. There are lots of possible answers to this question. Make sure yours includes full paragraphs which argue for and against having mobile phones in schools. Your ideas should be linked together using plenty of links of contrast, addition and number.

Section 5 – Writing Style

Pages 36 and 37 – Repetition in Fiction Writing

1. There are lots of possible answers to this question. Make sure yours includes an explanation as to how the repeated words, phrases and clauses create the mood in the extracts.
   Example:
   First extract: The repetition of 'cannon' suggests the hopelessness of the situation as everywhere they look there are cannons.
   Second extract: The repetition of 'fog' creates a threatening mood, as you can't escape from it and it attacks people.

2. There are lots of possible answers to this question. Make sure yours include repetition to create the mood shown in brackets. Examples:
   (dangerous) In caves where darkness crept around corners, where darkness tapped you on the shoulder, where darkness whispered and moaned at you.
   (happy) The king was joyful that the Sun was shining, joyful that the feast was almost ready and joyful that his crown was gleaming.
   (gloomy) Wind made the hedgerows shiver, made the trees whine, and made the clouds gather and plot great mischief.

3. There are lots of possible answers to this question. Make sure yours use repetition of words, phrases and clauses to create the mood you chose in the box.

Pages 38 and 39 – Useful Techniques in Non-Fiction Writing

1. **During the 19th century** — Fronted adverbial
   It helps to set the scene for the passage.
   who visited the area after reading Wordsworth's poetry about its wild, romantic beauty — relative clause
   It gives more information about the tourists who came to the Lake District.
   after reading Wordworth's poetry about its wild, romantic beauty — subordinate clause
   It tells the reader why the tourists came to the Lake District.
   its wild, romantic beauty — expanded noun phrase
   It describes how Wordsworth portrayed the Lake District in his writing.

2. Any suitable passage which uses a variety of phrases and clauses to connect the notes from the box.

3. There are lots of possible answers to this question. Make sure yours makes reference to and explains why you chose to use the clauses and phrases in your answer to Question 2.

Pages 40 and 41 – Non-Standard English in Written Speech

1. going to, come on, alright, give me, let me, cup of, because, lot of, isn't it

2. 'I'm gonna hit you if you don't lemme have it! Gimme the money.'

3. wee — little
   boggin' — dirty
   tidy — good
   daps — pumps
   bairn — baby or child
   owt — anything
   mardy — sulky or grumpy
   blower — phone

4. There are lots of possible answers to this question. For example, local words for 'bread roll' include 'bap', 'bun', 'barm' and 'cob'.
   Friendly forms of address such as 'mate' or 'dear' have the local words 'pet', 'me duck' and 'kidda'.
   Local words for 'alley' include 'ginnel', 'snicket' and 'jitty'.
   Local words for 'you' when talking to more than one person include 'yous' and 'you lot'.

5. I don't want to do any more work today. I've been working for hours. Let me go and play with my friends. Come on, give me a break, Mum!"

Answers

6. Any suitable explanation. Example:
Most of the time, you should write in Standard English. However, you can use non-Standard English in written speech to show how a character sounds and what they actually say when they speak.

End of Grammar Quiz

Pages 42 and 43

1. Series, crises, deer *[1 mark]*
2. 'Water' = verb, 'plants' = noun,
'or' = conjunction,
'the' = determiner or article, 'weekly' = adverb,
'they' = pronoun
[1 mark]
3. "If I <u>had gone</u> to Dad's last weekend, we were going to watch the match, but he had to go away instead," said Kai. "Now he (has broken) his foot, so we can't go next weekend either. (We've both been) unlucky."
[1 mark]
4. There are lots of possible answers to this question. Some different examples are shown below:
I **could / should** do my homework tonight, but I don't want to. I **may / might / could** leave it till tomorrow, or I **might / may / could** just do it on Sunday. *[1 mark]*
5. You should have underlined the following parts of the sentence: <u>that were growing in the garden</u> and <u>which was enormous</u>.
There are several possible ways to punctuate the sentence. Examples:
The weeds that were growing in the garden, which was enormous, by the way, had spread over all the flower beds.
OR: The weeds that were growing in the garden (which was enormous, by the way) had spread over all the flower beds.
OR: The weeds that were growing in the garden — which was enormous, by the way — had spread over all the flower beds.
[1 mark]
6. There are lots of possible answers to this question. Examples:
You can borrow my guitar if you look after it.
You can borrow my guitar provided that you look after it.
You can borrow my guitar as long as you look after it.
[1 mark]

7. You should have underlined: 'which has ravaged your village'. You should have circled: 'provided that I can defeat him'. *[1 mark]*
8. There are lots of possible answers to this question. Example:
After we walked up the hill, we sat down and ate lunch. (There should be a comma after the subordinate clause.)
[1 mark]
9. Jan stopped his lorry <u>suddenly</u> <u>in the middle of the road</u>. 'suddenly' is an adverbial of time
'in the middle of the road' is an adverbial of place
<u>When he got out</u>, he could hear a helicopter <u>overhead</u>.
'When he got out' is an adverbial of time
'overhead' is an adverbial of place
[1 mark]
10. There are lots of possible answers to this question. Example:
You might want to use non-Standard English when you are showing how a character actually speaks.
[1 mark]

Punctuation

Section 6 – Sentence Punctuation

Pages 44 and 45 – End of Sentence Punctuation

1. Any suitable answer. Example:
From outside the stone walls of the castle came ghostly shrieks. Bea and her dog Bouncer quivered in terror at the thought of what might be waiting. Then, without warning, came silence. This was even worse.
2. Any suitable explanation. Example:
The passage is easier to follow after it has been split up into shorter sentences. The shorter sentences also help to build tension.
3. Could you move**?** **T**he road isn't wide enough for two cars.
The decorator made a mess when painting**.** **P**edestrians were told to avoid the wet paint.
4. Any suitable explanation. Example:
At the moment, the sentence means that they washed up their grandparents as if they were plates. A full stop needs to be added after the word 'up', so that the current sentence is broken up into two shorter sentences.

Answers

Pages 46 and 47 – Parenthesis

1. You should have matched these pairs:
   Elephants live in Asia and Africa. — the largest land mammals
   My singing performance was a disaster. — filmed by Dad
   I pulled out Granny's gift and tried to look grateful. — the orange jumper
   Our new puppy chews everything. — an adorable poodle
   Any suitable rewriting of the sentences with the parenthesis placed between commas, dashes or brackets. Examples:
   Elephants, the largest land mammals, live in Asia and Africa.
   My singing performance — filmed by Dad — was a disaster.
   I pulled out Granny's gift (the orange jumper) and tried to look grateful.

2. Any suitable answer. Examples:
   Brazil (a country in South America) is home to the Amazon Rainforest.
   Someone — we were never sure who — knew about what we'd done.
   Gavin, my best friend, plays the guitar and the drums.
   The plant (not the one on the table) was a gift from our neighbour.

3. Any suitable answer. Examples:
   The professor, **exhausted from the experiment**, threw the equipment across the laboratory and howled in rage.
   The money we raised — **almost £20** — was enough to buy a card and a large bunch of flowers.
   Both of the countries (**Norway and Canada**) have long coastlines.

4. Any suitable explanation. Example:
   The brackets have not been used properly because the sentence doesn't make sense without the parenthesis.

Page 48 – Abbreviations

1.

Full length word / words	Abbreviation
Mister	Mr
Great Britain	GB
Professor	Prof.
minimum and maximum	min. and max.
kilometre	km
Saint or Street	St
September	Sept.
miles per hour	mph
New York City	NYC
teaspoon	tsp

Section 7 – Commas and Apostrophes

Page 49 – Commas Around Embedded Clauses

1. You should have matched these pairs:
   Cumbria has many mountains and lakes. — where my friend lives
   Bob decided he would try baking a cake. — who is a terrible cook
   My sister wants to learn how to drive. — who is nearly 17
   Any suitable rewriting of the sentences with the subordinate clause placed within the main clause. Examples:
   Cumbria, where my friend lives, has many mountains and lakes.
   Bob, who is a terrible cook, decided he would try baking a cake.
   My sister, who is nearly 17, wants to learn how to drive.

Pages 50 and 51 – Commas with Co-ordinating Conjunctions

1. You should have matched these pairs:
   My phone's battery is flat — we'll have to use yours.
   Annie's dog looks fierce — he's actually a big softy.
   We could go for a pizza — we could have a burger.
   Any suitable rewriting of the main clauses as one sentence joined with a comma and a co-ordinating conjunction. Examples:
   My phone's battery is flat, **so** we'll have to use yours.
   Annie's dog looks fierce, **but** he's actually a big softy.
   We could go for a pizza, **or** we could have a burger.

Answers

2. You should have added a comma to these sentences:
   The squirrel forgot where the acorn was buried, so in the spring a tree grew.
   Sally had to cross the muddy field, yet she arrived with a smile.
   Una entered her drawing into the competition, and later she received a letter saying that she had won.

3. There are lots of possible answers to this question. Make sure yours is correctly punctuated and has a suitable title. Example:
   Title: Between Storms
   The storm has moved on, but the wind still blows.
   The ground is still sodden, and the fog still hangs.
   More dark clouds approach, so the rain still falls.
   Another storm is coming, yet the Sun still shines.
   The landscape looks warm, but it's bitterly cold.
   The wind shakes the trees and howls on the moor.
   It's getting darker now, so I know it's getting close.
   A storm has moved on, yet another arrives.

Pages 52 and 53– Commas to Avoid Confusion

1. While painting, children should take extra care.
   All winter, animals took shelter from the snow.
   In the room above, the waiter served the food.
   Tomorrow at four, twenty guests will arrive.
   OR: Tomorrow at four-twenty, guests will arrive.

2. Any suitable explanations. Examples:
   With a comma, the sentence means that kindness is good, whereas without a comma, the sentence means that kindness is not good.
   With the pair of commas, the sentence means that it is Arthur who thinks that the teenager should have helped the old man with his shopping.
   With a pair of commas, the sentence means that Henry plays rugby, but Daniel doesn't.

3. Any suitable explanation. Examples:
   My heroes are my parents, Mo Farah, and Queen Elizabeth.
   This sentence is better punctuated because it's clear that their parents aren't Mo Farah and Queen Elizabeth.
   We ate onion soup, spicy chicken, and mango ice cream.
   This sentence is better punctuated because the first sentence sounds like the ice cream is made from spicy chicken and mango.
   In the park we saw two squirrels, Mr Smith, and Dr Sidhu.
   This sentence is better punctuated because it's clear that the speaker saw two squirrels as well as Mr Smith and Dr Sidhu.

Page 54 – Commas Between Adjectives

1. You should have added a comma to this sentence:
   She was told to expect an amusing, handsome man.
   All of the other noun phrases should have a tick in the box next to them.

2. There are lots of possible answers to this question. Examples:
   a ripe, juicy tomato
   a colourful spotted sweater
   some tasteless, lumpy custard
   an enormous polar bear

Page 55 – Punctuating Interjections

1. Well, that was a lovely meal. — **tick** (correctly punctuated)
   'Wow', is a word that is spelt the same backwards. — **cross** (incorrectly punctuated — should not have a comma)
   Oh, I think I've lost my glasses. — **tick** (correctly punctuated)
   No, dogs were allowed on the field. — **question mark** (you can't tell — without a comma it means that dogs weren't allowed, with a comma it means 'on the contrary, dogs were allowed')
   Isla, can't help us because she's visiting her gran. — **cross** (incorrectly punctuated — should not have a comma)

2. Any suitable examples followed by a suitable explanation. Examples:
   Kerry, we have to go home now.
   Kerry! Thank goodness you've come back!
   The difference is that the second sentence sounds more urgent and dramatic than the first sentence.

Page 56 – Commas for Places and Dates

1. The concert was held on 24th August, 2016.
   On Princes Street, Edinburgh, there is a large art gallery.
   In the summer of 2012, the Olympic Games were held in London, England.

2. Any suitable explanation. Example:
   The comma makes it clearer that Downing Street is in London.

3. There are lots of possible answers to this question. Make sure yours includes a fronted adverbial which includes a date. Example:
   On 15th May, 2011, my sister got married.

Answers

Page 57 – Apostrophes

1. You should have added apostrophes to these sentences:
   Whose job is it to feed Amy's hamster while she's away? It's hungry.
   We weren't ready for the start of the race, and the girls' team beat us easily.
   In the players' changing room, the goalkeeper's shirt was on a bench.

2. Any suitable answers. Examples:
   I won't help you hide Dana's coat; it's not a nice thing to do.
   Who's the man taking the dogs' bone away?
   I'm not going to clear up Sarah and Kate's mess.
   I won't eat Miles's cake.

Page 58 – Homophones involving Apostrophes

1. Does **your** mum know **you're** staying late?
   Who's to know **whose** coat this is?
   They're not unveiling **their** new car yet.
   Look, **it's** licking **its** paws.
   They've rung to say **they're** on **their** way.

2. There are lots of possible answers to this question. Examples:
   Don't forget to make your lunch.
   I think you're a terrible singer.
   My socks aren't as nice as theirs.
   That's the man whose wife is a nurse.
   The bird protected its chicks from the hawk.

Page 59 – Apostrophes – Tricky Plurals

1. You should have added apostrophes to these sentences:
   In three days' time, I will be seeing my cousins again.
   This candidate has five years' experience in computer programming.

2. You should have corrected these phrases:
   mens' toilets — men's toilets
   no mans land — no man's land
   sheeps wool — sheep's wool
   the womens faces — the women's faces

Section 8 – Punctuation for Speech

Pages 60-62 – Punctuating Speech

1. Any suitable answers. Examples:
   Rick whispered urgently, "There are some very dark clouds in that sky."
   "Hurry up," **barked Angela angrily.** "We're going to be late."

2. There are lots of possible answers to this question. Example:
   "Stop that car!" screamed Sayid and Jamala, running as fast as they could towards the road. "They've stolen our cat!"

3. "I've no idea where we're going," moaned Adam. "I keep tripping over."
   Monty yelled, "If you don't hurry up, Bella will have eaten all the cake!"
   "Isn't it a beautiful sunset?" Mum said to me as we got out of the car.
   "Hey, be careful!" said Sara, patting the trembling little dog. "Can't you see that he's really scared and nervous?"
   (In this pair of sentences, the first sentence of speech can be written in several different ways — e.g. it might have a comma where the exclamation mark is in the example answer above.)

4. "When I went to my new school, I really hated it," admitted Lily, wiping away tears, "and each time my teacher opened the door, I ran away."

5. Any suitable answers. Examples:
   Inverted commas are used to show any words that are spoken.
   A reporting clause is a clause like 'she said' or 'he shouted'. It tells you who said something and how they said it.

6. "Look over there!" shouted Maia, pointing to the top of the tree. "I'm sure that's a dinosaur I just saw."
   "Don't be ridiculous," replied her mum, rolling her eyes crossly. "There are no dinosaurs living today. They all died out millions of years ago."
   "No they didn't," Maia argued, opening her book and showing her mum a brightly-coloured picture. "They just evolved into birds."

Page 63 – Reported Speech to Direct Speech

1. Any suitable rewriting of the passage in direct speech. Example:
   Kai said to Rhiann, "I'm a bit annoyed with you."
   "Why are you annoyed with me?" said Rhiann. "What have I done?"
   "My bike is old and rusty, and I wish you'd remembered to bring it in out of the rain," Kai said to her.
   Any suitable extension of the passage using direct speech. Example:
   Rhiann replied, "I didn't know your bike was outside, Kai."
   "Yes you did," he snapped. "You saw me leave it in the garden when I came inside."

Answers

Pages 64 and 65 – Direct Speech to Reported Speech

1. "Marco, could you pass me that blue bowl?" asked Nadia.
   Nadia asked Marco to pass her the blue bowl.
   "Don't look behind you," Tom warned Ellen.
   "There's a ghost there!"
   Tom warned Ellen not to look behind her because there was a ghost there.
   "We'd better not go in," I said to my cousins.
   "The floor looks rotten."
   I told my cousins that we had better not go in because the floor looked rotten.

2. There are lots of possible answers to this question. Examples:
   Dad told us to hurry up or there would be nowhere to park.
   Joe told me he had gone to football the night before and had broken his ankle.
   Eve said the history homework from last week was really hard.

3. There are lots of possible answers to this question. Examples:
   "Put your coat on," Dad said.
   Dad told me to put my coat on.
   "Have you seen my comic?" asked Jed.
   Jed asked if she had seen his comic.

Section 9 – Paragraphs and Layout

Pages 66 and 67 – Paragraph Structure

1. Any suitable rewriting of the paragraph. Example:
   When we arrived at the museum at Caerleon, our guide greeted us and took us through to the museum. After walking through the baths, we arrived in a room of Roman items, many of which we were studying at school. The guide gave us costumes so we could dress up as Romans. They were very scratchy. After we'd seen everything in the museum, we went to the shop to buy a souvenir.

2. There are lots of possible answers to this question. Make sure yours includes three paragraphs of information organised in a clear, logical order.

3. Any suitable explanation based on your answer to Question 2.

Pages 68 and 69 – Paragraphs: New Speaker, New Line

1. You should have added these paragraph markers:
   "I'm a bit fed up," I admitted, "actually." // "Oh dear, why is that, then?"
   "The last time I was in a school play, the scenery fell down on top of the choir." // "That sounds exciting, but was anyone hurt?" // "No!"
   "We need to be careful," explained the wizard, "as the next part of our journey is both difficult and dangerous." // "Will we meet any pixies?" asked Robin. // "I don't know, we might do. They won't harm us if we sing to them as we pass them." // "Oh. It's a shame I can't sing then."

2. Any suitable dialogue with new lines for each change of speaker and reporting clauses where needed. Example:
   "Let's make a cake for Mum's birthday," suggested Svenya.
   "Last time we did it there were eggs all over the floor," mused Natalie, "and she was furious when she came home."
   "But we're older now and we won't make a mess," replied Svenya, proudly.
   "OK, then, let's get on with it. We'll have to hurry though to get everything tidy before she get back."
   "Don't be daft!" said Svenya. "She won't be cross on her birthday. Now you get the butter and eggs from the fridge, and I'll get the flour and the weighing scales."

End of Punctuation Quiz

Page 70 and 71

1. Example: The prizes (silver cups, medals and shields) were displayed on a shelf in her bedroom. (Dashes are also acceptable for the parenthesis.) *[1 mark]*

2. Since Bindi hated tidying more than she hated mess, it fell to Mari, who was always incredibly tidy, to do it for her. *[1 mark]*

3. **They're** not feeding the goat. **You're** feeding it, since it's yours. *[1 mark]*

4. The **cabbages** and **leeks** in the grocer's shop **were** fresh. *[1 mark]*

5. "**I** don't know what you think you're doing with my chain," said the ghost, "but it's my job to rattle it."
   [2 marks — 1 mark for correct use of speech marks, 1 mark for all other punctuation being correct]

Answers

6. You should have ticked the following sentences:
I opened the fridge but couldn't find any milk. (second sentence of the pair)
The school had new computers, and teachers made the most of them. (second sentence of the pair)
As soon as he arrived at the fair, he saw all his friends. (first sentence of the pair) *[1 mark]*

7. There needs to be a new line when there is a change of speaker. *[1 mark]*

8. There are lots of possible answers to this question. Any correctly punctuated direct speech sentence using the given words is acceptable. Example:
"No thanks," she gulped. "I can manage on my own."
[2 marks — 1 mark for correct use of speech marks, 1 mark for all other punctuation being correct]

Spelling

Section 10 – Prefixes

Page 72 – Number Prefixes from Latin

1. 80
   4
   1
2. **multi**tasking
   centenary
   trilogy
3. biped: human, bird
   quadruped: mouse, hippo
   centipede: centipede
   I think the Latin root 'ped(e)' means **foot/leg**.

Page 73 – Prefixes: 'mini' and 'micro'

1. **micro**organisms, **micro**scope, **mini**bus, **mini**skirt, **micro**wave, **micro**phone
   The **microphone** was unnecessary — everyone could hear Asha's voice without it.
   We cooked the popcorn in the **microwave**.
   Microorganisms can be responsible for causing sickness.
   The **miniskirt** was a little tight around the waist.
   Under the **microscope**, we could see the tiny insect's antennae.
   Our teacher drove us in a **minibus** to the match.

2. Any suitable sentences. Examples:
   At the zoo I saw some **miniature** ponies.
   We need to **minimise** the damage this causes.
   Paula did the **minimum** amount of work to pass the test.
   The fish were so **miniscule** I could barely see them.

Page 74 – Prefixes: 'bene' and 'mal'

1. **malaria** — A deadly disease which is spread by mosquitoes.
   benefit — Advantage taken from something.
   malnutrition — Illness caused by a lack of good food.
   malformed — Something that is poorly shaped.
   benefactor — Someone who offers assistance or charity.
2. Any suitable reason, for example:
   The audience would think that Benvolio is a 'good' character whereas Malvolio is a 'bad' character.

Page 75 – Prefixes: 'ultra' and 'hyper'

1. The **ultramarine** colour of her dress was very eye-catching.
   Bats make an **ultrasonic** click that humans struggle to hear.
   I was **hypersensitive** to the pollen and started to sneeze immediately.
   The captain pressed a button to send the rocket into **hyperspace**.
2. You should have circled: **ultrasound**, **hyperactive**, **ultraviolet**.
3. Example:
   Hyperthermia means **having a body temperature that is too hot**.

Page 76 – Prefix: 'fore'

1. Many years ago, when our **forefathers/forebears** moved to this land, it was **foretold** (or **forecast/foreseen**) that one day a hero would be born. The people would recognise him by a scar on his **forehead** just above his eyebrows, and an unusually short **forefinger** on his left hand.
2. Any suitable sentences. Examples:
   Susan fell over and broke one of the bones in her **forearm**.
   My grandfather always said that forewarned was **forearmed**.

Answers

3. There are lots of possible answers to this question. Example:
I think the term adage means **that if you know about something in advance you are better prepared to deal with it.**
A situation in which this could be used is **when you go on a trip, it's good to find out what the weather is going to be like so you can take appropriate clothing.**

Section 11 – Word Endings and Suffixes

Page 77 – Suffixes: Changing to Verbs

1. -en: lighten, harden, sadden, frighten, widen, darken, straighten
-ify: glorify, simplify, horrify, amplify, notify, classify, justify
-ise: realise, hospitalise, authorise, computerise, equalise, advertise
-ate: assassinate, captivate, motivate, activate, medicate, elasticate, decorate

2. Any suitable sentence. Example:
We are going to computerise our files in an attempt to simplify them.

Pages 78 and 79 – Suffixes: the Sounds of 'shus' and 'shul'

1. '-cious' / '-tious': delicious, nutritious, vicious, ambitious, cautious, suspicious, conscious, conscientious, precious, superstitious, malicious.
'-cial' / '-tial': facial, special, initial, potential, essential, financial, beneficial, confidential, artificial, residential, commercial.

2. Any five sentences containing a word from Question 1.
Example: Apples are nutritious.

3. Something you really need is **essential**
This is to do with where you live. **residential**
Someone who really wants to be successful is **ambitious**
Someone who won't walk under a ladder is **superstitious**
This is to do with money. **financial**
Someone who always does their duty is **conscientious**

4. atrocity, suspicion (or suspect), benefit, office, commerce, confidence, essence

Pages 80-82 – Suffixes: 'ant', 'ent' and their variants

1.

Root	-ation or -ential	-ant or -ent
preside	**presidential**	**president**
vary	**variation**	**variant**
apply	**application**	**applicant**
expect	**expectation**	**expectant**
reside	**residential**	**resident**
torr-	**torrential**	**torrent**
jubil-	**jubilation**	**jubilant**

2. resistance, coherence, performance, preference

3. You should have ticked:
"I don't know why you're looking so innocent! You broke it!"
He's such an arrogant person — it's hard to like him, actually.

4. obedi**ent**, instrum**ent**, developm**ent**, perman**ent**, dorm**ant**, achievem**ent**, flu**ent**, anci**ent**, contest**ant**, relev**ant**, signific**ant**, judgem**ent**, indiffer**ent**, extravag**ant**, triumph**ant**

5. You should have circled: influence, difference, vacancy, emergency, tendency, efficiency

6. I can't see any real evid**ence** that aliens have landed on Earth.
She doesn't have much experi**ence**, so she's finding it hard.
Lenny was reading a book about artificial intellig**ence**.
He will need some guid**ance** to be able to carry out that task.
Use the dictionary for refer**ence** when you do the homework.
"I have no more pati**ence** with your mess," yelled Mum.

7. Any five sentences containing some words that end in 'ance', 'ence', 'ancy' and 'ency'.

Section 12 – Confusing Words

Page 83 – Words Containing 'ei' and 'ie'

1. soc**ie**ty, fr**ie**nd, consc**ie**nce, perc**ei**ved, for**ei**gn, sc**ie**nce, effic**ie**ncy, rec**ei**ve, conc**ei**ved, suffic**ie**nt, l**ei**sure, rec**ei**pt

Answers

2. I hope to **receive** the book I ordered by next week.
   They **conceived** a plan to solve all the problems.
   Only thirty miles to the gallon is quite poor fuel **efficiency**.
   I want to return a dress I bought, but I can't find the **receipt**.
   Michael **perceived** a change in his father's mood.

3. Any suitable sentence. Example:
   The ancient sovereign ate protein at his leisure, and made weird counterfeit machines that were neither sufficient nor efficient.

Pages 84 and 85 – Words Containing Double Consonants

1. -cc-: o**cc**upy, a**cc**ording
   -pp-: a**pp**arently, a**pp**reciate, o**pp**ortunity
   -gg-: a**gg**ressively
   -mm-: co**mm**unity, i**mm**ediately

2. The cat hissed **aggressively** at the vet.
   According to the map, we have nearly reached our destination.
   I **appreciate** your hard work and all the help you have given me.
   We will put a plaster on your knee at the first **opportunity** we get.
   If you hear the alarm, **immediately** leave the building.
   The scouts met in the **community** hall.
   Apparently, it was Zara who told Rob I was scared of spiders.

3. bri**ll**iant, co**rr**espond, reco**mm**end, emba**rr**ass, exa**gg**erate, su**ff**icient, su**gg**estion, co**mm**unicate, co**mm**i**tt**ee

4. Any suitable mnemonics. Example:
   marvellous: **M**y **A**unt **R**ita **V**alues **E**ither **L**azy **L**lamas **O**r **U**gly **S**heep

Page 86 – Silent Letters

1. lis**t**en, dou**b**t, me**c**hanic,
   s**w**ord, autum**n**, **p**sychology,
   desi**g**n, fas**c**inate, r**h**ythm

2. You should have made the words: **gho**st, kn**ob**, m**or**tgage, disci**p**le, an**s**wer, cu**p**boar**d**, **w**riggle, kni**gh**t
   hidden message: **good work**

Page 87 – The Many Sounds of 'ough'

1. nought — brought
   plough — bough
   cough — trough
   thorough — borough

2. Any suitable words Examples:
   scruff — **rough**
   slow — **dough**
   true — **through**
   scout — **drought**
   sport — **thought**

3. There are lots of possible answers to this question.

End of Spelling Quiz

Pages 88 and 89

1. The correct order is:
   uni – bi – tri – oct – dec – cent – mille *[1 mark]*

2. miniature, microchip (or microprocessor) *[1 mark]*

3. Any answer which demonstrates that 'beneficial' is associated with 'goodness', and 'maleficent' is associated with 'badness' or 'evil'.
   Examples:
   A beneficial diet is one that **does you good.**
   A maleficent person **does evil deeds.**
   [1 mark]

4. You should have underlined <u>ultrasound</u> and <u>hypertension</u>. *[1 mark]*

5. electrify, darken, medicate, apologise, identify, threaten
   [1 mark]

6. initial, precious, special, gracious *[1 mark]*

7. observant, confident, coherent, expectant
   [1 mark]

8. I **perceive** he has deceived me about the **weight** of the **piece** of pie. *[1 mark]*

9. dou**b**tful, as**th**ma, **w**rench, mus**c**le, **p**terodactyl, solem**n** *[1 mark]*

10. enough, rough, dough, noughts, cough *[1 mark]*

End of Book Test

Pages 90-95

1. prepositions: on, by
   determiners: his, that, the
   pronouns: he, it
   [1 mark]

2. simple past: found OR picked OR told
   past progressive: was walking
   present perfect: have decided
   past perfect: had (never) seen
   [1 mark]

Answers

3. Any sentence which includes a modal verb (can, may, shall, will, must, could, might, should or would) and the word 'fly'. *[1 mark]*

4. **W**hen she was dressed**,** **J**amila ran downstairs**,** hoping **M**ax **(**her friend who was often late**)** would have arrived**.** **S**he and **M**ax were going to **B**en**'**s house for his birthday party.
   Acceptable punctuation for the parenthesis 'her friend who was often late' are commas, brackets or dashes.
   [2 marks — 1 mark for correct punctuation of the parenthesis, and 1 mark for all other correct punctuation]

5. 'Fore' means **'before' or 'at the front'**.
   Example sentence: **There were rose bushes in the foreground of the picture.**
   [1 mark]

6. Ella**'**s dog**'**s naughty. He**'**s always growling at you and it**'**s scary. *[1 mark]*

7. You should have circled the following spellings:
   Initially, performance, brilliant, admitted and exaggerated. *[1 mark]*

8. There are lots of possible answers to this question.
   Examples:
   First thing in the morning, the small group of soldiers on horseback galloped up the hill towards the derelict castle.
   Safely anchored in the cove, the fisherman pulled his nets into the boat and inspected his catch.
   There must be commas after both fronted adverbials to get the mark. *[1 mark]*

9. possibility: could, might and may
   obligation: should, must
   [1 mark]

10. There are lots of possible answers to this question.
    Examples:
    Last night, a bright light, pulsing and glowing deep red, shone through my window and woke me.
    Last night, a bright light, which was pulsing and glowed deep red, shone through my window and woke me.
    [1 mark]

11. knitting, climb, subtle, rustle, muscle, honour
    [1 mark]

12. Example:
    "Mum, Rex has dug up all your carrots," said Dai, "and he's sitting in the garden chewing one."
    [1 mark]

13. You should have ticked the following two sentences:
    She ate lunch and then had a bowl of ice cream.
    Don't eat sweets now: we're having dinner later.
    [1 mark]

14. terrorise, intensify, lengthen, captivate *[1 mark]*

15. influ**e**nce (**influential**)
    subst**a**nce (**substantial**)
    ess**e**nce (**essential**)
    [1 mark]

16. Any three pairs of sentences that use the homophones correctly. Examples:
    'You're going to fall off that chair.' / 'Your cake is cooked.'
    'They're looking for the dog.' / 'It's their ball.'
    'It's very cold today.' / 'Give the dog its dinner.'
    [3 marks — 1 mark for each pair of sentences with the homophones used correctly]

17. Examples:
    The train **we were waiting for** was late.
    Tamsin, **who really loved sport,** was not a good swimmer but was extremely good at football.
    [1 mark]

18. "Don't you like science?" asked Ahmed. "I love it: it's so much fun burning things and blowing them up."
    "I just find it really dull," replied Jack. "I'd rather be out on the football field or playing rugby. Science doesn't interest me."
    [2 marks — 1 mark for correct direct speech punctuation, and 1 mark for a new line for each change of speaker]

19. Examples:
    She has to do that test even if she doesn't want to.
    Provided that the train isn't cancelled, we intend to go to the match.
    [1 mark]

20. A relative clause: 'who loves history and culture.'
    A fronted adverbial: 'Thanks to its many priceless works of art'
    [2 marks for finding a correct example of both features, or 1 mark for finding a correct example of 1 feature]